The 244th Royal Academy of Arts Summer Exhibition
4 June – 12 August 2012

D1634543

Summer
Exhibition
List of Works
2012

Sponsored by

Insight
INVESTMENT

➤ A BNY MELLON COMPANY℠

Royal Academy of Arts

Contents

Sponsor's Preface

Insight Investment is proud to continue its association with the Royal Academy of Arts, a partnership that reflects values shared by both institutions: quality and creative thinking.

The Royal Academy strives continually to interest its visitors with thought-provoking works of art that stimulate their imaginations. Insight's focus is on providing clients with innovative solutions to meet their evolving investment needs.

Launched in 2002, Insight is responsible for £170 billion* in assets under management for a wide range of investors, including pension funds, corporates, sovereign wealth funds, insurers and private individuals. Our philosophy is to deliver consistent and repeatable performance for our clients through focusing only on doing those things we can do well. This has allowed us to build a reputation for excellence in liability risk management, fixed income, multi-asset and absolute return investments.

This year, our seventh as lead sponsor of the Royal Academy's Summer Exhibition, is a very special year. As the eyes of the world turn on London as it celebrates The Queen's Diamond Jubilee and the Olympic Games, the Summer Exhibition is showcasing contemporary British art alongside a large number of works submitted from overseas.

We hope that all visitors to the Summer Exhibition, together with Insight's clients, business partners and colleagues, will share our passion and find inspiration in the talent and creativity on display.

Abdallah Nauphal
Chief Executive Officer

Insight
INVESTMENT

➤ A BNY MELLON COMPANY℠

---

* Insight's assets under management are represented by the value of physical securities and present value of liabilities subject to hedging strategies.

Royal Academy of Arts in London, 2012

Registered Charity No. 1125383. Registered as a company limited by guarantee in England and Wales under Company No. 6298947

6

Dr Jennifer Dickson
Kenneth Draper
Jennifer Durrant
Prof Tracey Emin
Prof Stephen Farthing
* Peter Freeth
Antony Gormley OBE
Piers Gough CBE
Anthony Green
Spencer de Grey CBE
Sir Nicholas Grimshaw CBE PPRA
Zaha Hadid CBE
Nigel Hall
David Hockney OM CH
Gary Hume
Prof Paul Huxley
Timothy Hyman
Bill Jacklin
* Tess Jaray
* Eva Jiricna CBE
Allen Jones
Anish Kapoor CBE
Michael Landy
Christopher Le Brun PRA
Richard Long
Sir Richard MacCormac CBE
Prof David Mach
Prof Ian McKeever

John Maine
Lisa Milroy
Prof Dhruva Mistry CBE
Mick Moon
Mali Morris
David Nash OBE
* Humphrey Ocean
Hughie O'Donoghue
* Prof Chris Orr MBE
Cornelia Parker OBE
Eric Parry
Grayson Perry
Tom Phillips CBE
* Dr Barbara Rae CBE
Prof Fiona Rae
David Remfry MBE
Prof Ian Ritchie CBE
Mick Rooney
Jenny Saville
Alan Stanton
Gillian Wearing OBE
* Alison Wilding
* Chris Wilkinson OBE
Prof Richard Wilson
Bill Woodrow
John Wragg

* *Hanging Committee 2012*

Honorary Members

Antiquary: James Fenton
Chaplain: The Revd Lucy Winkett
Professor of Ancient History:
    Prof Sir John Boardman FBA
Professor of Ancient Literature:
    Prof Eric Handley CBE FBA
Professor of History of Art:
    Prof Dawn Ades OBE FBA
Emeritus Professor of History of Art:
    Vacant

Professor of Law: Sir Alan Moses
Emeritus Professor of Law:
    The Rt Hon The Lord Hutchinson
    of Lullington QC
Secretary for Foreign Correspondence:
    The Rt Hon The Lord Carrington
    KG GCMG CH MC PC
Corresponding Members:
    Mrs Drue Heinz HON DBE
    Sir Simon Robertson

Awards and Prizes

A total of £64,000 is offered in awards and prizes for every category of work in the Summer Exhibition

The Royal Academy of Arts Charles Wollaston Award
£25,000 to be awarded by a panel of judges appointed by the President and Council for the most distinguished work in the exhibition.

The Lend Lease/Architects' Journal Awards
£15,000 donated by Lend Lease: £10,000 Grand Award for Architecture; £5,000 for the best work by a first-time exhibitor in the Summer Exhibition.

The Jack Goldhill Award for Sculpture
£10,000 for a sculpture.

The Sunny Dupree Family Award for a Woman Artist
£3,500 for the best painting or sculpture.

The Arts Club Trust Award
£2,000 awarded to an artist aged 35 or under for a work in any medium except architecture.

The London Original Print Fair Prize
£2,000 for a print in any medium.

The Hugh Casson Drawing Prize
£1,500 for an original work on paper in any medium, where the emphasis is clearly on drawing.

The British Institution Awards
Four prizes of £1,000 each are awarded by the Trustees of the British Institution for Promoting the Fine Arts in the United Kingdom, which was established in 1805 to encourage the study of the fine arts. Students entering paintings, works on paper, sculpture and architecture will be eligible for the awards.

The Rose Award for Photography
£1,000 for a photograph or series of photographs.

Submission and Sale of Works

The Summer Exhibition

The Royal Academy's Summer Exhibition is the largest open contemporary art exhibition in the world, drawing together a wide range of new work by both established and emerging living artists. Held annually since the Royal Academy's foundation in 1768, the Summer Exhibition is a unique showcase for art of all styles and media, encompassing paintings, sculpture, prints, film, photography and architectural models. An essential part of the London art calendar, the show draws over 150,000 visitors during its three-month run. Some 1,200 works are included and, following long Academy tradition, the exhibition is curated by an annually rotating committee of Royal Academicians, who are all practising artists and architects. The majority of works are for sale. Any artist may enter work for selection.

Entering works

An artist is entitled to submit a maximum of two works. If you are interested in entering work for next year's Summer Exhibition, details may be obtained from the Royal Academy's website, www.royalacademy.org.uk, from January 2013. Alternatively, please send a C5-sized stamped, addressed envelope to the Summer Exhibition Office, Royal Academy of Arts, Burlington House, Piccadilly, London W1J 0BD.

Sales of works

All prices are inclusive of VAT where applicable. Spots are used to indicate that a work is sold. The Royal Academy levies a commission of 30% (plus VAT) on sales. A deposit equal to the commission will be taken by the Academy when the offer to purchase is registered. Cheques, credit cards and cash are all acceptable. Upon notification by the Academy, the artist will contact the intending purchaser to formally accept the offer and request the balance of payment. If for any reason the artist does not accept the offer, the commission will be returned to the purchaser by the Academy at the purchaser's request. All arrangements for the payment of the balance and collection or delivery of the work are made between the artist and the purchaser. If the purchaser resides outside of the United Kingdom he or she must bear the transportation and importation costs. A VAT-registered artist is required to provide the purchaser with a VAT invoice.

Editions coming from abroad

Please be aware that purchasing editions by artists who live abroad may incur extra transportation/importation costs, and in this event these costs must be met by the purchaser. All artists' addresses are listed in the back of this book and are printed on the Offer to Purchase.

Collection of purchased works	All exhibited works must remain on display until the exhibition closes. Towards the close of the exhibition the artist, having received the balance of payment from the intending purchaser, will forward a signed Removal Order to the purchaser. The purchaser may collect the work from the Royal Academy on production of this card between Saturday 18 August and Friday 7 September 2012, Monday to Friday between 8 am and 4 pm, and on Saturdays between 9 am and 4 pm. Collection cannot be made on Sundays or on Monday 27 August (bank holiday).

The artist will send unframed editions of prints directly to the purchaser once the artist has received the balance of payment.

Please be aware that there may be disruption to your journey during the collection period due to specific transport arrangements for the Paralympic Games. Please visit www.tfl.gov.uk/orn for more information. |
| **Intellectual property rights** | Under the Copyright, Designs and Patents Act 1988 it is the general rule that, in the absence of any agreement to the contrary, copyright in a work of art belongs to the artist, or to his or her heirs and assigns. The artist also enjoys certain moral rights for the term of copyright, i.e. the rights of paternity and integrity. |
| **Academy Framing offer** | As a special offer, prints purchased from the Summer Exhibition will be framed, on production of the sales receipt, at a 15% discount on the normal cost of framing. |

Current and Future Exhibitions

CELEBRATING THE QUEEN'S DIAMOND JUBILEE
The Queen's Artists
John Madejski Fine Rooms
Until 12 August 2012

The King's Artists: George III's Academy
Tennant Gallery
Until 21 October 2012

FROM PARIS
A Taste for Impressionism: Paintings from the Clark
Sackler Wing of Galleries
7 July – 23 September 2012

ARTISTS' LABORATORY 05
Hughie O'Donoghue RA
Weston Rooms
29 August – 21 October 2012

BRONZE
Main Galleries
15 September – 9 December 2012

ARTISTS' LABORATORY 06
Stephen Chambers RA
Weston Rooms
7 November – 16 December 2012

Catalogue

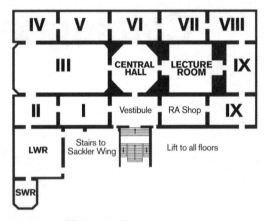

The Courtyard The Annenberg Courtyard

I Harry and Carol Djanogly Gallery

II Harry and Carol Djanogly Gallery

LWR Large Weston Room

SWR Small Weston Room

III The American Associates Gallery

IV

V The Jeanne Kahn Gallery

VI The Philip and Pauline Harris Gallery

Central Hall The Wohl Central Hall

VII The John Madejski Gallery

VIII The Weldon Gallery

IX The John A Roberts FRIBA Gallery

Lecture Room

X The Porter Gallery

The John Madejski Fine Rooms

Cloakrooms are
situated on the
ground floor

Courtyard

1 FROM LANDSCAPE TO PORTRAIT

£ 180,000

Engineered timber, stainless steel and concrete
Chris Wilkinson RA

Wohl
Central Hall

2 ASHTON'S PLUNGE £ 96,000
acrylic
Frank Bowling RA

3 FLOWERS COMING DOWN FROM THE SKY £ 19,000
oil
Philip Sutton RA

4 CHEMICAL TRACK £ 40,000
acrylic
Derek Boshier

5 BAMBOO GROVE WITH GREEN ENSO £ 24,000
acrylic
Maurice Cockrill RA

6 PINK CITY £ 5,500
oil on canvas
Philippa Stjernsward

7 06.01.11 NFS
gloss and matt paint on composite aluminium board
David Batchelor

8 SELF-PORTRAIT VENICE £ 35,000
oil
Ken Howard RA

9 DARTMOUTH, THE FERRY £ 2,500
oil on panel
Frederick Cuming RA

10 RUSHLIGHT £ 4,850
acrylic
Mali Morris RA

11 CLUMP SOUL £ 845
oil
Stephanie Theobald

12 ALWAYS FOREVER £ 1,400
oil
Mark O'Rourke

13 SCENE £ 2,950
ink, watercolour, gouache and soft pastel on paper
Dan Perfect

14 THE ARTIST AT WORK £ 13,500
oil
Thomas Ryan

15 RETAIL £ 150
acrylic
Michelle Ranson

16 STREET IN BATH £ 380
oil
Francis Callaghan

17 27/6/1976 £ 120,000
acrylic
The late John Hoyland RA

18 29/4/1973 £ 120,000
acrylic
The late John Hoyland RA

19 POSTCARD FROM PROVENCE II £ 16,000
oil
Sonia Lawson RA

20 RICHARD SHERIDAN IV (1962–2001) NFS
acrylic
Frank Bowling RA

21 FIRST LOVE (BABES IN THE ATTIC) £ 4,200
oil
Timothy Hyman RA

22 WAKING AT DAWN, SHINGLE STREET   £ 3,675
oil
Timothy Hyman RA

23 WINTER LIGHT   £ 600
acrylic on board
John Fitzmaurice

24 KIMONO   £ 40,000
oil
Dame Elizabeth Blackadder RA

25 AFTER THE FLOOD   £ 1,650
acrylic and watercolour
David Gould

26 UNDER THE RAIN   £ 2,000
mixed media
Louise McClarey

27 PUDDLE PAINTING: PALE LILAC, YELLOW   £ 54,000
(AFTER BONNARD)
acrylic on stainless steel
Ian Davenport

28 EVENING LIGHT   £ 8,500
acrylic
John Wragg RA

29 HOUSE OF DREAMS   £ 8,500
acrylic
John Wragg RA

30 WAITING TO KNOW   £ 8,500
acrylic
John Wragg RA

31 DUET   £ 16,000
oil
Eileen Cooper RA

32 CHISWICK HOUSE   £ 8,000
oil
William Bowyer RA

33 HAMMERSMITH BRIDGE
£ 12,500
oil
William Bowyer RA

**34 FIRST CAMELLIAS OF THE SEASON, STRINGS
FROM THE IRONING BOARD**
£ 9,500
oil
Diana Armfield RA

**35 LEISURELY LUNCH AT THE ROYAL SHIP,
DOLGELLAU**
£ 10,500
oil
Diana Armfield RA

36 CAMELLIAS ON THE EASEL
£ 7,500
oil
Diana Armfield RA

37 A REHEARSAL
£ 10,000
oil
Bernard Dunstan RA

38 REHEARSAL: THE HARP
£ 9,000
oil
Bernard Dunstan RA

**39 SERIES 'GHIRLANDA CONTINUA': AFTER
LATVIA NO. 4, LETTER E**
£ 6,500
acrylic
Jennifer Durrant RA

40 ULTIMA ORA
£ 15,000
egg tempera
David Tindle RA

41 EVENT HORIZON
£ 4,200
oil and acrylic on linen
Govinda Sah 'Azad'

42 STOURHEAD, 30TH JUNE
NFS
oil
The late Adrian Berg RA

43 REMBRANDT BOOK MARK
£ 8,000
oil
Martin McGinn

44 THE ALCAZAR, SEVILLE, FROM THE HOTEL 18TH, 19TH AND 20TH MARCH NFS
watercolour pencil and crayon
The late Adrian Berg RA

45 KEW GARDENS 23RD OCTOBER (2) NFS
watercolour pencil and crayon
The late Adrian Berg RA

46 2ND LAKE, SHEFFIELD PARK GARDEN, SUSSEX WEALD, LATE SUMMER NFS
oil (diptych)
The late Adrian Berg RA

47 THE EDGE OF COLOUR £ 2,950
giclée print
Brigitte Williams
(edition of 10: £2,300 each)

48 FLOWERS £ 15,000
oil
John Bellany RA

49 FINESTRA VENEZIANA FONDAMENTA ZATTERE AL PONTE LUNGO £ 50,000
acrylic, glass, lattino glass relief on wood relief
Joe Tilson RA

50 EARLY MORNING PEMBROKESHIRE £ 17,500
oil
Philip Sutton RA

51 THE SAD-FACED DON QUIXOTE... £ 9,500
oil
Philip Sutton RA

52 WINCHESTER £ 2,500
handmade paper and acrylic
Sheila Girling

53 CATCH AUGUST £ 2,900
oil
Marilyn Hallam

54 THE SLIPWAY £ 8,000
oil
William Bowyer RA

55 PORTRAIT OF A YOUNG MAN STANDING £ 600,000
polished bronze
Leonard McComb RA
(edition of 10: £600,000 each)

56 UNTITLED £ 1,000
oil
Neil Raitt

57 IBM THINKPAD £ 850
relief cast in concrete
Robin Tarbet
(edition of 3: £850 each)

58 OUT OF ORDER £ 360
oil and card on canvas
Leslie Farago

59 DRINKING WATER £ 1,850
oil and acrylic
The Baron

60 PETROL STATION ON ROUTE 17 NEAR £ 2,300
KANKANAMODDI
mixed
Danny Pockets

61 FRIENDS NEEDED! £ 1,200
oil
Robert Eisner

62 MILONGA £ 9,000
oil
David Remfry RA

63 STUDIO DOOR TO THE GARDEN £ 3,500
egg tempera
David Tindle RA

64 IF CHAIRS COULD TALK £ 620
oil
Anna Hymas

65 GOLEUNI
£ 1,200

acrylic on MDF
Elfyn Lewis

66 SERVER
£ 2,000

oil on linen
Alex Hudson

67 CANDY
£ 1,500

oil
Dunisha Samarasinghe

68 WILLOW LAND I
£ 480

oil
Amanda Ansell

69 YELLOW ARCHITECTURAL ANATOMY
£ 1,250

acrylic
Ron Sims

70 TOWARDS CHURCH
£ 200

acrylic
Anne Courtney

71 FOUNTAIN IN OLD OAK ROAD
£ 3,500

oil
Andrew Stahl

72 HORSE WITH NO NAME
£ 1,200

pencil and oil on melamine surface
Elizabeth Vicary

73 SIT DOWN PROSE
£ 850

watercolour
Rachel Heller

74 DAPPLED SUNSHINE BY THE NANTHIR
£ 5,000

oil
Diana Armfield RA

75 GOLDEN AFTERNOON IN THE RHYD YR EFAIL FIELDS
£ 5,000

oil
Diana Armfield RA

76 STUDY FOR SELF-PORTRAIT PAINTING IN THE GARDEN £ 4,000

egg tempera
David Tindle RA

77 KING AND QUEEN £ 250

acrylic
Thomas Waters

78 TIAN £ 1,950

acrylic
Emyr Williams

79 JOYRIDE £ 2,850

acrylic
Silia Ka Tung

80 THOUGHTS £ 2,940

oil
Yalda Noori

81 BASANT £ 3,500

pure pigment and gesso
Rani Gilani

82 UNTITLED (FROM THE 'TRANSITION POINT' SERIES) £ 350

screenprint on perspex
Luna Jung–Eun Lee
(edition of 3: £280 each)

83 SING-ALONG MICROPHONE £ 2,000

acrylic on perspex
Silia Ka Tung

84 ORCHESTRAL REHEARSAL £ 8,000

oil
Bernard Dunstan RA

85 SUNSHINE ON A FROSTY MORNING, BY LLWYNHIR £ 7,500

oil
Diana Armfield RA

86 WE MUST GO DOWN TO THE SEA AGAIN £ 1,300
oil
Brenda Evans

87 GONE WITH THE WIND £ 550
acrylic
Aude Grasset

88 POWERS £ 2,835
oil
Malina Karimi

89 DISLOCATION £ 100
ink, watercolour and collage
Aimée-Beth Warburton

90 CLIFF TOP SHEEP 3 £ 3,000
encasutic wax and pigment on board
Terry Setch RA

91 METTA £ 980
oil
Andrea McLean

92 DANDELION SUMMER £ 5,500
oil
Jeffery Camp RA

93 SOMALILAND £ 1,600
mixed media
Matthew Corbin Bishop

94 INTRUSION 3 £ 2,250
mixed media
Henny Acloque

95 FLORAL £ 5,500
oil
Jeffery Camp RA

96 DANYA £ 600
oil and concrete
Fiona Long

97 THE GOLDEN ISLAND £ 5,000
oil on panel
Richard Cartwright

98 NARCOTICS £ 3,150
oil and sawdust
Mohammad Daud Hedayati

99 TONE £ 2,835
poster paint
Nabila Horakhsh

100 A GLYPHIC FRAGMENT £ 4,500
oil on metal
Neil Jeffries

101 UNTITLED £ 1,060
acrylic
Robert Welch

102 THE ENLIGHTENMENT £ 1,500
oil
Dominic Shepherd

103 DERBYSHIRE FARMS £ 1,250
oil
Terence Bennett

104 CAPUT MORTUUM £ 950
ink, pencil, caput mortuum pigment
Toby Wiggins

105 BEANS ON TOAST £ 500
oil
Amanda Coleman

106 INTERIOR, EASTERN AVENUE £ 900
oil
Julian Mitchell

107 NORTH WEST COAST £ 1,800
oil on linen
Hilary Elmes

108 COUPLE £ 3,800
acrylic on nettel
Owusu-Ankomah

109 VULCAN £ 800
acrylic and enamel on cardboard
Steve Ferris

110 FEMME À MOUSTACHE NFS
gouache
Selma Gurbuz

111 LUNGE £ 750
oil
Gabriella Boyd

112 LH £ 2,900
oil on zinc
Nadia Hebson

113 BUTTOCKS VASE £ 1,500
oil on zinc
Paul Becker

114 BOY WITH GAS MASK £ 4,600
oil on board
Gideon Rubin

115 A STROLL OR A PADDLE £ 250
acrylic on wood
Vanessa Whitehouse

116 SOFT-CORE £ 1,500
mixed media on wood
David Small

117 UNTITLED (OBJECTS) £ 2,000
acrylic
Celia Hempton

118 RISE £ 450
cut paper
Toni Davey

119 THE LAST RETREAT £ 2,200
oil and acrylic on canvas
Lee Madgwick

120 THE GUIDANCE COUNSELLOR £ 2,900
(FOR WILLIAM GOLDING)
oil on linen
Michael Ajerman

121 BIG NUMBER £ 12,500
acrylic on linen
Richard Smith

122 APERITIF-PARIS £ 725
oil
Allan Samuels

123 A MINI DRAMA: NUMBERS SERIES: £ 75
MEASURING: NO. 114240605912
collage
Suzanne Lykiard

124 POLITE ROOM II £ 500
oil, acrylic and charcoal on paper
Seokyeong Kang

125 CHAMBER MUSIC £ 8,000
oil
Bernard Dunstan RA

126 BLUE 3A £ 600
aluminium and brass
Francis Coen

127 RED 3B £ 600
aluminium and steel
Francis Coen

128 EPIPHANY £ 8,000
mixed media
Tony Carter

129 DREAM OF MISS WILLMOT'S ORCHARD, £ 500
TRESSERVE
oil
Kate Yates

130 TEAR OUT THE BAD STUFF £ 350
aquarelle on paper
Ylva Ziverts

131 R FOR RENTED £ 7,000
oil on dismantled beer crate
Oliver Clegg

132 WINDSWEPT £ 4,800
oil
Eileen Cooper RA

133 OTHERS I £ 2,500
pencil, watercolour and gouache on card
Aishan Yu

134 ORIENTAL ROTUNDA AND INTERIOR £ 1,250
acrylic
Ron Sims

135 CATHEDRAL £ 1,200
oil
David Stokes

136 LINEAR COLOUR I £ 195
glass
Hildegard Pax
(edition of 5: £195 each)

137 BUILDING £ 5,000
ink on tracing paper
Susan Hefuna

138 EAU DE NIL £ 300
mixed media
Pauline McCabe

139 LEE £ 2,500
acrylic
James Judge

140 FISH FOUNTAIN £ 3,500
oil
Andrew Stahl

141 UNTITLED £ 800
oil and acrylic on canvas board
Michael Kennedy

142 THE MYSTICAL £ 350
merinos wool felt
Loriana Scarnicchia

143 ONE WAY OR ANOTHER £ 6,200
oil
Simon Burton

144 CLIFF TOP SHEEP 4 £ 3,000
encaustic wax and pigment on board
Terry Setch RA

145 RIDGEWAY PATH £ 1,200
oil
Tim Woodcock-Jones

146 INNER CHAOS £ 1,800
acrylic and oil on board
Nicholas McLeod

147 IMAGINARY PORTRAIT OF PAOLO UCCELLO £ 2,400
(1994–2012)
acrylic, graphite and pumice
Geoffrey Rigden

148 THE CLEVER YOUNG MAN £ 1,250
egg tempera on gesso
Robin-Lee Hall

149 X-WING £ 850
oil on board
Simon Wright

150 HOMAGE TO BOETTI £ 595
giclée print
Brigitte Williams
(edition of 100: £295 each)

151 THE SEA £ 895
oil
Lucy Giles

152 HARAM ALEIKUM £ 2,000
mixed media
Fathi Hassan

153 DOPPELGÄNGER / FREISCHWIMMER £ 3,500
acrylic
Jost Münster

154 DESPERATE TO BE AMAZED £ 10,000
acrylic
Derek Boshier

155 LAGUNA SAN IGNACIO £ 1,950
acrylic
David Webb

156 THE VOID £ 450
acrylic
Aude Grasset

157 FIGURE I £ 195
mixed media
Valerie McLean

158 LAURICA £ 2,000
acrylic on board
Louis Nixon

159 LOVE £ 600
pencil and ink
Francesca Lowe

160 TOWARDS YANWORTH £ 500
oil
Karen Bowers

161 PASS £ 2,200
oil
Nick Sargent

162 A GIRL, ALMOST #1 £ 3,000
acrylic
Maurice Cockrill RA

163 A GIRL, ALMOST #2 £ 3,000
acrylic
Maurice Cockrill RA

164 FISH £ 1,500
oil
Michael Whittlesea

165 DISGUISES OF JAQUES MESRINE NO. 5 £ 350
oil on board
Toby Ursell

166 YONDER (DIPTYCH) £ 7,700
oil
Jane Harris

167 DUCK EGGS £ 1,500
oil on linen
Sarah Gillespie

168 LANDSCAPE IN WARWICKSHIRE £ 1,500
oil
Timothy Gatenby

169 ROAM £ 1,700
oil on board
Perienne Christian

170 RISE £ 1,800
oil on board
Perienne Christian

171 THE GOLAN HEIGHTS VIEW FROM MY BALCONY £ 2,200
oil on board
Naomi Alexander

172 NERVES £ 1,600
oil, pencil and copper leaf on chalk gessoed panel
William Stein

173 STOPFTWIST COTTON BOX £ 3,800
found cotton box, paper, card and enamel
Sarah Bridgland

174 SONGBIRDS £ 1,725
balsa wood, paper, card and enamel
Sarah Bridgland

175 RAINBOW TREE NFS
acrylic
Poppy Sendell

176 NOT THAT FAR FROM ELGIN MARBLES £ 220
archival digital print on rag paper
Nevill Wilson
(edition of 20: £180 each)

177 PLUG £ 650
oil on board
David Woodall

178 FERMATT £ 350
mixed
Kasper Pincis

179 MEASURING TO KNOW £ 950
oil and wax on board
Patrick Adam Jones

180 BURNING LIGHT, SUNSHINE DRAWING SERIES £ 850
burnt paper
Julia Hutton

181 POLYPOLYPHEMUS £ 525
acrylic
Jennifer Harding

182 MARZIA £ 2,800
acrylic
Gina Medcalf

183 CONDITIONS 01 (IRIS) £ 950
giclée print
Alexandra Hughes
(edition of 5: £790 each)

184 SCHEIDEGG MIT JUNGFRAU £ 350
mixed
Kasper Pincis

185 ATLANTIS £ 350
oil on linen
Maximilian Ghose

186 BEDFORD BRICKWORKS, SYDNEY, NFS
NEW SOUTH WALES, AUSTRALIA
needlepoint in stranded cotton
Teresa Forrest

187 PICTURESQUE BATHROOM, RATISBON £ 1,680
oil
Timothy Hyman RA

188 CONNECTICUT: PATHWAY £ 3,000
oil and acrylic on aluminium
Ben Ravenscroft

189 BAGHDAD (NIGHT) £ 7,500
mixed media
Mohammed Gharbawi

190 HOLDING MYSELF TOGETHER SO FAR, £ 600
AND NO SIGNIFICANT BLEEDING
hand embroidery on linen
Effie Jessop

191 PEG TAPESTRY £ 6,000
oil, wooden pegs and chicken wire
Annie Morris

192 NEW ZEALAND £ 1,600
mixed media
Matthew Corbin-Bishop

193 MIXED INTERACTIONS THROUGH SPACE £ 3,000
acrylic, paint and MDF
Olly Fathers

194 TREES AT SUNRISE, PROVENCE £ 10,000
oil
Leonard McComb RA

195 ALONG THE RIDGE £ 3,500
(BUCOLIC HIPPY SERIES NO.9)
oil on linen
Clyde Hopkins

196	**SPRUNG POSER**	£ 5,000
	oil	
	Jeffery Camp RA	

197	**A LINE DRAWING**	£ 1,800
	oil	
	Jeff Gibbons	

198	**RECOUNTING, NO. 1**	£ 3,600
	mixed media	
	Taraneh Hemami	

199	**RECOUNTING, NO. 9**	£ 3,600
	mixed media	
	Taraneh Hemami	

200	**TAKING A CALL**	£ 1,000
	oil	
	Lance Fennell	

201	**FLIGHT / DISPATCH (TWINS)**	£ 3,750
	oil and pens	
	Virginia Verran	

202	**FALLING LIGHT**	£ 1,250
	oil	
	Francis Bowyer	

203	**BLOSSOM**	£ 10,000
	oil	
	Lucy Jones	

204	**PATH THROUGH TREES WITH SNOW**	£ 595
	tempera	
	Alexander Adams	

205	**BEN SLEEPING**	£ 450
	oil	
	Marcus Austin	

206	**NEWS**	£ 1,450
	newspaper	
	Fabiana di Mascio	

207 FORM £ 750
gloss paint
Marc Goodwin

208 BAGHDAD (DAY) £ 7,500
mixed media
Mohammed Gharbawi

209 LISTEN – ORANGENESS £ 600
oil
Richard Kenton Webb

210 THE SONG OF THE DENTIST'S SON - £ 600
EARTH ORANGE-RED
oil
Richard Kenton Webb

211 ECHI DI IME £ 6,000
clay and burlap
Nnenna Okore

212 BIRDS £ 900
acrylic
Luciana Meazza

213 EXTERIOR £ 3,200
oil on embroidered canvas
Nick Sargent

214 NIGHTFALL 1, VERBIER £ 475
oil
Jacqueline Weir

215 NAILS SERIES FORM II £ 1,990
concrete and scaffold nails on timber
Naomi Doran

216 TREES IN MORNING LIGHT £ 445
mixed media
Maxine Hart

217 ON THE ROAD – SPAIN, 13 £ 675
oil on linen
Liz Bailey

218 CAKE LADY NFS
acrylic
Susanna Negus

219 INFLATE II £ 2,000
white emulsion on canvas with nylon gland and plastic tube
Natasha Kidd

220 NOON £ 2,300
acrylic, wood, hessian, pins, Montana spray paint
Flore Nove-Josserand

221 IN BETWEEN £ 1,700
oil on linen
Marguerite Horner

222 CONTAINED £ 500
enamel and gloss
Angela Smith

223 UNTITLED (FLOWERS) £ 1,500
oil on linen
Nadia Hebson

224 FORBIDDEN £ 550
oil on panel
Michael O'reilly

225 KNIFE AND FLY £ 340
oil
Richard Swann

226 FIVE COLOUR PAINTING I £ 1,400
acrylic on birch-faced plywood panels
Nigel O'Neill

227 WHERE WHITE IS THE COLOUR £ 2,900
acrylic
Jeff Dellow

228 RIDER £ 1,800
oil on linen
Alex Hudson

229 ROCKY LANDSCAPE II AFTER LEONARDO £ 300
oil
Anne Webb

230 HOUSE WORK £ 1,200
cotton and silk
Caren Garfen

231 ROCK £ 450
oil on board
David Woodall

232 SERVANT OF THE MOON Editions available for sale
woodcut
Liam Ryan
(edition of 500: £15 each)

233 MINSMERE I £ 240
etched aluminium and woodcut
Kim Edwards

234 JEFFERSON (ORANGE) £ 8,400
oil, acrylic and silverpoint
Alison Turnbull

235 COLLECTION ONLY, NO. 40 £ 975
oil on calico
Richard Baker

236 GREEN, YELLOW AND GREY WITH PINK £ 32,000
AND CREAM (DUTCIA POTS III)
oil
David Stubbs

237 SUSPENSION £ 3,500
mixed media
Wendy Smith

238 PENANCE-WALL DRAWING NO. 1 £ 11,000
paper, watercolour, gesso and gold leaf
Cathy de Monchaux

239 VERNAL LAYER £ 2,900
acrylic
Jeff Dellow

240 STRAW MAN (AFTER GOYA) £ 2,800
oil on board
Neal Jones

241 TABLE £ 4,000
egg tempera
David Tindle RA

242 COLLAGE ON FILM (LA CHAPELLE) £ 790
c-type print
Alexandra Hughes
(edition of 6: £790 each)

243 FROM WHERE I'M LOOKING £ 2,000
silk on linen
Miranda Argyle

244 THE WINDOW £ 5,000
acrylic
John Wragg RA

245 REUNION II £ 8,400
acrylic
Albert Irvin RA

246 TERRA INCOGNITA £ 4,500
acrylic mediums and pigments on linen
Colette Morey de Morand

247 TWIST OF FATE £ 4,500
acrylic mediums and pigments on linen
Colette Morey de Morand

248 THE CAR £ 5,000
acrylic
John Wragg RA

249 ARCHANGEL £ 3,850
acrylic
Gus Cummins RA

250 LIGHT INTERIOR £ 4,800
acrylic and collage on canvas
Anthony Whishaw RA

251 CONTROL: FIGURES 1–3; 15.00, 19.00, 14.00 £ 920
gesso and pigment on plywood, silk and shellac-based ink
Lisa Peachey

252 REAL GHOSTS £ 2,200
oil on linen
Farah Syed

253 THE HUNDREDTH MONKEY /
MENEZES RIOT, NO.2 £ 2,200
oil
Alejandro Ospina

254 LONDON PAINTING (LEAVING TOWN) £ 17,500
oil, household gloss and acrylic
Rachel Howard

255 CARBON £ 350
acrylic
Tim Waskett

256 PIGEON £ 1,800
oil on panel
Stephen Rose

257 BUILDING F £ 4,200
acrylic on board
Ayman Baalbaki

258 REMEMBERING MY MOTHER £ 1,000
oil
Mohd Norhakim Yahya

259 HUG MY SOUL £ 895
oil
Matthew Kolakowski

260 PIECE OF MY HEART £ 1,250
acrylic on board
Martin Grover

261 ANOMALY I £ 1,700
oil
Peter Bill

262 AGAIN, AGAIN, AGAIN (PENCIL) £ 12,000
acrylic, oil, pencil and wax on linen on wood
Andrew Bick

263 HISTORY PAINTINGS: JONES GALLERY, £ 4,500
VICTORIA AND ALBERT MUSEUM #2
oil
Kevin Leathem

264 THE HUNT (AFTER UCCELLO) £ 4,000
oil on wood
Neal Jones

265 ALDEBURGH II - THE ARTIST AT THE £ 12,000
SOUTH LOOKOUT
oil on MDF
Anthony Green RA

266 AGENCY £ 1,800
mixed media on wood
David Small

267 ENGLAND A CENTURY OF CHANGE £ 700
old books, ink and beeswax
Ann Winder-Boyle

268 SHE'S LEAVING HIM £ 1,295
gesso, acrylic and oil on board
Jo Oakley

269 GROVE £ 14,400
oil
Christopher Le Brun PRA

270 RUMS YARD £ 1,200
mixed media
Orlanda Broom

271 LANDSCAPE WITH THREE BREASTS £ 950
acrylic
Derek Woolston

272 BLUE BLUE £ 1,600
copper carbonate pigment on CNC cut MDF panel and wall
Onya McCausland

283 FRAGRANCE IN THE WIND £ 200
acrylic
Michelle Ranson

284 COUNTY FAIR £ 4,500
oil on metal
Neil Jeffries

285 ARTIST £ 2,000
oil
Jasper Joffe

286 COLOUR AND SPACE £ 825
acrylic on canvas
Peter Kalkhof

287 WILD HORSE £ 2,000
acrylic on board
Louis Nixon

288 FOR AN EYE £ 1,750
oil on canvas
Alice Browne

289 NIGHT LIGHTS (NOCTURNAL) £ 1,500
oil on linen
Nick Carrick

290 MUTATIS MUTANDIS IX £ 4,800
acrylic
Paul Huxley RA

291 ANIMA ANIMUS VIII £ 4,800
acrylic
Paul Huxley RA

292 STUDIO TABLE £ 1,450
oil
Michael Whittlesea

293 (WORKING DETAILS) OFF THE WALL £ 3,850
acrylic
Gus Cummins RA

294 PAPER AND STREET (PAIR) £ 8,000
acrylic, Indian ink, enamel and varnish on canvas;
acrylic, gouache and oil on canvas
Phoebe Unwin

295 VIGILANT DREAMER £ 9,000
oil
Andrzej Jackowski

296 LENS / ASKEW (FOR ROSIE) £ 8,000
acrylic and mixed media
Ciaran Lennon

297 WORK NO. 1353 £ 27,600
oil on canvas
Martin Creed

298 TREMBLING LIKE DAMAGED RETINAS £ 5,400
Oil and acrylic
Alison Turnbull

299 UNTITLED £ 600
collage
Anne Harild

300 UNTITLED £ 950
acrylic and emulsion on panel
Rose Davey

301 ARCADIA £ 900
oil on linen
Caroline Kha

302 CHESS PAINTING NO.4 (SPASSKY VS. FISCHER, £ 3,500
GAME 4, REYKJAVÍC, 1972)
gesso
Tom Hackney

303 RESTART £ 800
acrylic
Graham Boyd

304 FATAL ATTRACTION £ 1,500
acrylic
Chris Chapman

305 AFTER MALEVICH £ 10,000
cut-out (diptych)
Tess Jaray RA

306 UNTITLED (SMALL COLLAGE NO. 25) £ 4,500
mixed media on archive paper on board
Fiona Rae RA

307 MIRACLE TREE WITH SEED £ 1,000
(MORINGA OLEIFERA)
pressed specimen
John Newling

308 UNTITLED (SMALL COLLAGE NO. 27) £ 4,500
mixed media on archive paper on board
Fiona Rae RA

309 VOEWOOD £ 3,400
sunlight on wood
Roger Ackling

310 VOEWOOD £ 1,500
sunlight on wood
Roger Ackling

311 IMPRESSION OF SNOW: CONIFERS £ 595
tempera on canvas board
Alexander Adams

312 ORDER / DISRUPTION NO. 44–45 (DIPTYCH) £ 1,250
Indian ink pen and pencil on paper
Giulia Ricci

313 CITYSCAPE £ 455
resin
Thomas Clarke

314 THE HISTORY OF THE WORLD IN 39 ARCHES £ 2,000
ink
David Winthrop

315 THE COLOUR OF DEATH £ 3,150
oil
Shamsia Ommalbanin Hassani

316 CITY £ 1,500

oil on panel

Alicia Rothman

---

317 CENTRE OF BINARY RHYTHM (III) AT 23RD APRIL 2012 £ 3,000

oil, wax and silverpoint on card

James Hugonin

---

318 SHEDDING IDENTITIES £ 1,000

acrylic on polyester

Hayoung Kim

---

319 ANAEMIA £ 750

mixed media on wet and dry paper

Alison Rylands

---

320 A DIFFERENT ONE £ 5,000

oil on wood

Nicolas Demetriou

---

321 JAPANESE PLATE WITH FRUIT £ 24,000

oil

Dame Elizabeth Blackadder RA

---

322 UNTITLED £ 790

acrylic

Xiao Yu

---

323 STUDY IV (BELL 45) £ 3,900

acrylic

Hans Heinrich Sures

(edition of 25: £250 each)

---

324 YOUNG GIRL £ 850

watercolour

Michael Coe

---

325 EMPIRES NFS

wool

Alexis Nishihata

---

326 CONTEMPLATION £ 600

acrylic

Pennie Elfick

327	**HISTORY PAINTINGS: JONES GALLERY, VICTORIAN AND ALBERT MUSEUM #1** *oil* Kevin Leathem	£ 4,500
328	**GREENWICH** *oil* Jeffery Camp RA	£ 5,000
329	**UNTITLED** *mixed media* Gary Colclough	£ 800
330	**TOGETHER** *oil* Simon Dalby	£ 430
331	**BEETLE** *oil* Robert Dukes	£ 5,000
332	**LIPSTICK BUILDING NYC** *oil on panel* Jarrod Gabbitas	£ 800
333	**BETA** *acrylic* Albert Irvin RA	£ 3,600
334	**PAULE AT SINK** *oil on board* John Lessore	£ 2,100
335	**THE MAN WHO WAS A BIRD** *oil* Christopher Wood	£ 3,250
336	**HEAD 2** *oil* Nadine Feinson	£ 2,000
337	**TRANC 2 (WELSH TRANSLATION SLOW DEMISE UNTIL DEATH)** *clay* Kelly Campbell	£ 500

338 STICK THEORY £ 32,000
oil on panel
Tom Phillips RA

339 MID WEST SUMMER £ 325
mixed media
Chris Feakins

340 FOOT £ 1,150
acrylic on paper
Valeria Levy

341 BLOCK 31 FROM MY STUDIO £ 175
acrylic and collage
David Pearson

342 ON THE DOWNS £ 300
oil
Richard Swann

343 DECO TEAPOT £ 140
acrylic
Susanna Negus

344 BLACK TREACLE £ 1,500
egg tempera
Joel Penkman

345 THE VIRGIN REALISES SHE IS PREGNANT £ 50,000
pencil on paper
Victor Newsome

346 UTAH IV £ 2,000
oil on canvas
Mary Webb

347 GIRL WALKING £ 950
oil
Gabriella Boyd

348 WALK IN THE SOUQ £ 800
acrylic on board
Nicola Skinner

349 DIANA   £ 1,400
photograph
Raeda Saadeh
(edition of 10*)

---

350 COMPOSITION NO.2 – OBJECTS, COLOUR,   £ 1,250
SPACE – SERIES II
acrylic on card and wood
David Hensler

---

351 RUBBLE   £ 2,000
acrylic
Celia Hempton

---

352 SPANISH LANDSCAPE WITH FIVE ENCINAS   £ 175
acrylic and earth
David Pearson

---

353 BLACK BARN   £ 200
acrylic
Laurence Hobson

---

354 STREETLIFE   £ 780
acrylic
Robert Welch

---

355 PLANET II   £ 650
acrylic
Tim Cousins

---

356 AT A SLANT   £ 1,000
acrylic
Caroline de Lannoy

---

357 APPLE   £ 450
oil on wood
James Ng

---

358 MAN ON A BEACH BALL   £ 5,400
oil on canvas over board
David Sullivan

---

359 SEATED FIGURE   £ 5,000
acrylic
John Wragg RA

* Refer to Sales Desk

360 GLOOMY MOUNTAIN VIEW THANKFULLY £ 420
LIGHTENS UP SOMEWHAT
acrylic
Martin Ive

361 VOID £ 1,400
glazed ceramics
Karin Schösser

362 GOOD MORNING MS RIBERA £ 1,600
acrylic
Francisco Nicolas

363 CHANCE OF A LIFETIME £ 20,400
oil
Allen Jones RA

364 THE BLACK GATE, SOUTHWOLD £ 1,200
oil
Thomas Deakins

365 EL CATSO £ 2,000
acrylic
Edward Gooding

366 PINK TREE £ 25,000
oil
David Austen

367 INTERIOR (GREEN/SUNLIGHT/SHADOW) £ 4,000
oil on four panels with toughened glass
James Ross

368 CONCOURSE £ 4,500
oil
Morag Ballard

369 THE CLASSROOM £ 1,800
oil
Marguerite Ruffles

370 MILESTONE £ 1,300
oil on aluminium
Benjamin Clarke

371	**SAILBOAT IN THE CUT**	£ 1,500
	acrylic	
	Michael Miller	

372	**SUMMER SWIFTS**	£ 485
	acrylic on board	
	Julian Sutherland-Beatson	

373	**SOON AFTER STORM**	£ 2,200
	oil on canvas	
	Rodrigo Costa	

374	**BIRDCAGE I**	£ 850
	oil on panel	
	Kitty Stirling	

375	**GREET 2012**	£ 8,400
	acrylic	
	Albert Irvin RA	

376	**AT THE MILL**	£ 1,350
	oil on canvas	
	Tadeas Kotrba	

377	**HARE ON HILL**	£ 200
	acrylic and emulsion on found wood	
	Sally Welchman	

378	**COMPLEXITY OF ADULTHOOD 3**	£ 3,400
	acrylic on board	
	Miho Sato	

379	**RESTLESS CIRCLES #2**	£ 5,000
	oil	
	Carol Robertson	

380	**LUNARIA**	£ 6,500
	oil	
	Charlotte Verity	

381	**SHADES OF SUNSET**	£ 495
	collage	
	Juliana Sadeh	

382 RETIRED ORIENTAL PHILOSOPHER OUT JOGGING £ 6,000
acrylic
Frank Bowling RA

383 AND IONA'S GREEN £ 6,000
acrylic
Frank Bowling RA

384 FAMILY TREE £ 6,000
acrylic
Frank Bowling RA

385 SIXTY THREE (SELF) 2011 £ 1,200
oil and paper on board
Trevor Sutton

386 UNTITLED £ 500
embroidery cotton
Lara Punch

387 THE TAILOR'S DAUGHTER FROM BUNDI £ 1,100
acrylic on card
Staphan Sarkissian

388 LANDSCAPE ON LETTER CARD TO MRS TAYLOR £ 180
pencil, watercolour and ink on card
Marcus Leotaud

389 DUNWICH LATE SUMMER £ 1,500
oil
Jane Dowling

390 ARIA, NO. 12 £ 1,750
oil
Michael Bennett

391 SERIES 'GHIRLANDA CONTINUA': AFTER LATVIA NO. 5 £ 6,800
acrylic on canvas on board
Jennifer Durrant RA

392 FRIDGE £ 1,570
acrylic
John Butterworth

393 FRIEND £ 800
oil
Alison Pilkington

394 NEPTUNE IN PISCES £ 660
digital 3D colour print
Tom Lomax
(edition of 25: £660 each)

395 PAPPY'S £ 350
oil on panel
Sarah Ann Mitchell

396 THE THEATRE £ 1,200
oil paint and ink on wood
Charlotte Posner

397 FAÇADE £ 2,650
acrylic
David Webb

398 CHESS PAINTING NO.16 (DUCHAMP VS. £ 2,750
MENCHIK, PARIS, 1929)
gesso on linen
Tom Hackney

399 KIT A £ 850
oil on paper stretched over board
Louisa Mahony

400 BLUE £ 750
oil, acrylic, gouache and ink on paper
Greg Genestine-Charlton

401 MOUNTAIN GOATS £ 950
oil and varnish
Sam Douglas

402 STILL LIFE IN THE LANDSCAPE £ 240
acrylic
Hazel Leach

403 NO. 292 £ 2,400
paint on powder-coated aluminium
Rana Begum

404 BIPLANE £ 750
oil on board
Simon Wright

405 ECHO (FORBES WATSON) £ 2,500
oil and silver leaf on wood
Liz Rideal

406 DRIFTING £ 2,500
acrylic
Tim Allen

407 WINTER MORNING NO. 4 £ 700
acrylic on linen
Rufus Knight Webb

408 ON LINE £ 800
watercolour
John Rae

409 TWO SKIES £ 2,700
acrylic
Mali Morris RA

410 STACK / OVERLAP (PRIMROSE) £ 2,700
acrylic
Mali Morris RA

411 ROCKET RACER £ 1,850
oil on board
Chuck Monroe

412 HUDDLE £ 2,850
oil on board
Grace O'Connor

413 MAJESTIC PEP £ 7,850
oil on board
Phillip Allen

414 WIKES STREET, SPITALFIELDS £ 6,000
pastel
Anthony Eyton RA

415 FLIGHT PATH £ 600
oil
Deborah Burnstone

416 LUPUS LUPUS £ 15,500
oil, household gloss and acrylic
Rachel Howard

417 LAMB £ 1,400
oil on linen
Comhghall Casey

418 SHRINE TO TEDDY POM POM NFS
mixed media collage
Kate Haynes

419 UNTITLED (SMALL COLLAGE NO. 28) £ 4,500
mixed media on archive paper on board
Fiona Rae RA

420 DYSLEXIA £ 3,750
aluminium, graphite, resin and wood
Michael Coombs

421 TITUS £ 850
coloured pencil, crayon and wash
Jane MacEwan

422 CASSIE NFS
acrylic
Amie Douglas

423 PASTORAL SCENE NFS
oil
Noah Makower

424 LATE AFTERNOON SKY £ 500
oil on board
Hannah Robinson

425 THE END £ 88
plastic
Yosef Cohen
(edition of 400: £88 each)

426 TQ 31949 05471 £ 850
charcoal on Bristol Board
Peter Marsh

427 AN ENDEAVOR TO BRIDGE THE GAP £ 500
oil and charcoal
Emily Jane Cooper

428 TWO TREES £ 480
oil on board
Kate Wilson

429 NELSON'S RIVER £ 480
oil on board
Kate Wilson

430 TREE £ 425
mixed media
Perdita Sinclair

431 BLACK JUG £ 10,000
oil
Mary Fedden RA

432 RHYTHM OF LIFE £ 950
mixed media on wood
Melissa Alley

433 PORTOBELLO HARBOUR £ 2,200
oil on linen
Francis Matthews

434 LONDON, 17 £ 3,000
bitumen on powder-coated aluminium
Nathaniel Rackowe

435 BAD SIGNAL 2012 £ 2,500
oil and gloss paint on MDF
Alexis Harding

436 THINGS TO COME #12 £ 4,500
oil
Keith Wilson

437 OASIS OF SERENITY £ 550

oil on acrylic panel
Benjamin Bridges

438 NORMAN'S BAY £ 2,640

oil on linen
Tom Hammick

439 THE RING £ 80

animal bones and plaster
Olu Shobowale
(edition of 8: £80 each)

440 VINES UNDER TABLE MOUNTAIN £ 5,000

oil
William Bowyer RA

441 EAST BOLDRE IN THE SNOW £ 280

acrylic
Francis Callaghan

442 INTO TRAFALGAR SQUARE £ 2,625

oil
Timothy Hyman RA

443 NIWL Y BRYN £ 1,100

acrylic
Elfyn Lewis

444 STORM APPROACHES £ 4,000

encaustic wax and pigment on board
Terry Setch RA

445 LOOK IN £ 700

mixed media on canvas board
Andrew Pearson

446 PROMISING DAY £ 5,000

oil
William Bowyer RA

447 COLLECTION ONLY, NO. 37 £ 625

oil on calico
Richard Baker

448 GALLERISTS £ 3,000
oil, ink and varnish on board
Andrew Cranston

449 APRIL (HIC HABITAT FELICITAS) £ 5,200
oil
John Stark

450 ALDEBURGH I – THE SCALLOP £ 12,000
oil on MDF
Anthony Green RA

451 CORN COBS £ 1,500
oil
Olwyn Bowey RA

452 CHAIR £ 2,800
oil on board
John Lessore

453 THE GAMBLE £ 395
lithograph
George Shaw
(edition of 100: £250 each)

454 BATHROOM MIRROR £ 8,000
oil
Bernard Dunstan RA

455 ROSE BUD £ 4,000
oil
Jeffery Camp RA

456 SPEAR OF RAIN £ 950
oil
Janette Kerr

457 VOYSEY WORDS AND MUSIC £ 4,000
acrylic
Stephen Farthing RA

458 FELDSPAR £ 4,500
oil on board
Annabel Dover

459 FRANK'S CAFE SE1 £ 200
acrylic on wood
Terence Sole

460 VENICE QUINTET 11.11.11 £ 18,000
oil on board
Ken Howard RA

461 OPEN AIR AVIARY £ 4,250
gouache and tempera on paper
Mick Rooney RA

462 SUDDENLY THEY CAME INTO FOCUS, VOYSEY £ 4,000
acrylic
Stephen Farthing RA

463 LR £ 1,750
oil
Alice Browne

464 A GIRL, ALMOST #4 £ 3,000
acrylic
Maurice Cockrill RA

465 A GIRL, ALMOST #3 £ 3,000
acrylic
Maurice Cockrill RA

466 SOMETHING ABOUT A RABBIT £ 4,250
gouache and tempera
Mick Rooney RA

467 QUAYSIDE £ 600
oil
Deborah Burnstone

468 BILDUDALUR £ 170
inkjet print on PVC
Garðar Snæbjörnsson
(edition of 5: £170 each)

469 CHESS COMPUTER PROGRAM PLAYING ITSELF £ 400
ink on primed linen
Martin Abrams

470 COMPOUND £ 5,000
oil, acrylic and graphite on aluminium
Ben Ravenscroft

471 HEAD 2 £ 600
acrylic
Stephen Jaques

472 PORTAL £ 1,500
oil
Alex Gene Morrison

473 OGV (CANVAS NOSTALGIA) £ 12,000
acrylic, oil, pencil, watercolour and wax on linen on wood
Andrew Bick

474 WILDERNESS WALKS £ 3,000
mixed media
Wendy Smith

475 UNTITLED £ 250
oil
Juliet Lushington

476 ORDER / DISRUPTION PAINTING NO. 1 £ 800
laser engraved laminated board and acrylic
Giulia Ricci
(edition of 5: £800 each)

477 HEAD ROOMS £ 6,500
acrylic
Basil Beattie RA

478 CORRIDOR MOUND £ 6,500
acrylic
Basil Beattie RA

479 INTERIOR, WHITBY £ 1,200
oil
Julian Mitchell

480 ORE £ 5,000
oil, wood and pegboard
Norman Toynton

481 BLUE NIGHT £ 5,000
oil, wood and pegboard
Norman Toynton

482 EVERYTHING IS £ 300
oil on linen
Iain Stronach

483 AN OWNER, XXII £ 850
acrylic
Ilsu Hwang

484 MISS WILLMOTT'S GHOST (ERYNGIUM) £ 1,500
oil
Olwyn Bowey RA

485 TANKER, MARGATE £ 1,300
oil
Francis Tinsley

486 SUBTERRANEAN HEIGHTS £ 6,500
acrylic
Basil Beattie RA

487 ABOVE AND BELOW £ 6,500
acrylic
Basil Beattie RA

488 UDAIPUR £ 5,500
oil
Ken Howard RA

489 TALL SHIPS, MOONRISE £ 1,400
oil on panel
Frederick Cuming RA

490 VENETUS £ 1,200
acrylic
Vesna Milinković

491 CELESTIAL PRESENCES £ 950
mixed media on wood
Melissa Alley

492 ONCE UPON A TIME £ 950
oil
John Crossley

493 BREEZE BLOCKS £ 2,500
acrylic, paint and MDF
Olly Fathers

494 CELEBRATION £ 950
acrylic
Sheena Clarke

495 UNTITLED £ 250
oil
Juliet Lushington

496 WHITE SCARF £ 1,200
oil on linen
Michael Ajerman

497 DER RHEIN £ 1,000
oil on linen
William Wright

498 THE HERMITAGE £ 1,500
ink, pencil, English red earth
Toby Wiggins

499 TWO GIRLS PLAYING DIABLO £ 1,850
oil
Simon Quadrat

500 BUBBLE HIGH £ 450
book cloth, grey board and gampi tissue
Katherine Jones
(edition of 6: £450 each)

501 WESTERN TIBET £ 1,200
oil and varnish on board
Sam Douglas

502 UNFOLDING 2 – AN UNDERSTANDING £ 750
OF DRAWING AS DESCRIBED BY MATISSE
etching
Fianne Stanford
(edition of 20: £500 each)

503 HEAP, IX   £ 5,000
acrylic on paper
Mohamed-Said Baalbaki

504 HENRY   £ 20,000
mixed media
Maliheh Afnan

505 FAMILY £ 140
etching
Karolina Larusdottir
(edition of 75: £100 each)

506 DEAD SUNFLOWERS £ 1,400
screenprint
Barbara Rae RA
(edition of 125: £990 each)

507 E-MIGRATION – WILL I MAKE IT? £ 400
digital print and drawing
Joanna Ciechanowska
(edition of 10: £200 each)

508 OWEN'S VALLEY CA £ 6,500
archival pigment transfer print
Boyd & Evans
(edition of 10: £5,000 each)

509 MILLE FLEURS £ 570
intaglio
Farah Syed
(edition of 30: £430 each)

510 YESNABY £ 2,300
collagraph/etching
Barbara Rae RA
(edition of 20: £2,000 each)

511 SEA FENCE £ 1,435
screenprint
Barbara Rae RA
(edition of 125: £975 each)

512 VAUCLUSE £ 1,400

screenprint
Barbara Rae RA
(edition of 125: £990 each)

513 AUTO-ERRATIC £ 600

etching
Philip Naylor
(edition of 30: £480 each)

514 TIME FOR TEA £ 300

giclee print
Suki Cohn
(edition of 25: £200 each)

515 WINTER FIELD BY THE SEA £ 150

aquatint
Joan Dannatt
(edition of 10: £100 each)

516 THE SPACE BETWEEN – 5 £ 1,200

etching
Ann Christopher RA
(edition of 20: £1,000 each)

517 THE SPACE BETWEEN – 6 £ 1,200

etching
Ann Christopher RA
(edition of 20: £1,000 each)

518 THE SPACE BETWEEN – 4 £ 1,200

etching
Ann Christopher RA
(edition of 20: £1,000 each)

519 FIRE, NYC £ 4,500

monoprint
Bill Jacklin RA

520 ROAD WITH BIRDS VIII £ 4,500

monoprint
Bill Jacklin RA

521 LATE NIGHT STORIES II (BERLIN) £ 480
hand-finished linocut
Claas Gutsche
(edition of 30: £380 each)

522 CHARLIE Editions available for sale
etching
David Remfry RA
(edition of 100: £375 each)

523 LAROUSSE £ 2,000
cut encyclopaedia
Alexander Korzer-Robinson

524 INTO THE SEA AT NIGHT VI £ 4,500
monoprint
Bill Jacklin RA

525 KILNSEA: IN OBSOLESCENCE £ 230
cyanotype with silver foil debossing
Jim Hobbs
(edition of 50: £120 each)

526 NEAR STRUMBLE HEAD NORTH £ 390
PEMBROKESHIRE
etching
Austin Cole
(edition of 20: £330 each)

527 TIVOLI £ 4,160
woodcut on japanese unryushi paper
Gillian Ayres RA
(edition of 30: £3,600 each)

528 KATSURA £ 5,355
woodcut on japanese unryushi paper
Gillian Ayres RA
(edition of 15: £4,500 each)

529 ORCHESTRA £ 200
linocut
Peter Shread
(edition of 30: £150 each)

530 PAST – PRESENT £ 800
etching (three plates)
Jolanta Rejs
(edition of 7: £500 each)

531 BOBOLI £ 1,690
woodcut on japanese unryushi paper
Gillian Ayres RA
(edition of 50: £1,440 each)

532 TORRENT £ 270
woodcut
Martin Davidson
(edition of 30: £190 each)

533 MIRABELL £ 4,160
woodcut on japanese unryushi paper
Gillian Ayres RA
(edition of 30: £3,600 each)

534 DUSK, SAN GIORGIO MAGGIORE £ 450
woodcut etching
Simon Lawson
(edition of 50: £300 each)

535 FANTASTICALLY FLEXIBLE FENESTRATION £ 600
ink
Edward Cullinan RA

536 JUSTICE AND MAYHEM £ 1,025
lithography and screenprint
Chris Orr RA
(edition of 30: £850 each)

537 WELCOME TO THE ATOMIC AGE £ 1,025
lithography and screenprint
Chris Orr RA
(edition of 30: £850 each)

538 STILL LIFE II £ 260
photo etching and aquatint
James Seow
(edition of 50: £150 each)

539 RUN £ 450
woodcut
Emily Smith Polyblank
(edition of 50: £350 each)

540 PALMHOUSE 8 £ 650
woodcut print on kozo
Trevor Banthorpe
(edition of 5: £575 each)

541 PORTAL £ 1,400
toned silver gelatin print
Paul Hart
(edition of 12: £1,200 each)

542 FULL STEAM AHEAD! £ 1,025
lithography and screenprint
Chris Orr RA
(edition of 30: £850 each)

543 COMEDY £ 975
etching
Chris Orr RA
(edition of 30: £800 each)

544 WHITE BULL NEAR DELPH, WITH £ 2,500
CASTLESHAW ROMAN FORT BEHIND
pencil
John Hewitt

545 FICTION II £ 975
ultrachrome print
Phil Shaw
(edition of 45: £900 each)

546 THE BIRTHDAY £ 295
lithograph
George Shaw
(edition of 100: £250 each)

547 'TOOTSIE! DON'T SIT ON THE QUILT' £ 360
inkjet print
Anthony Green RA
(edition of 100: £300 each)

548 BUTTERFLY GIRL £ 2,100

chalk and ink
Ivor Abrahams RA

549 PAESAGGIO £ 5,400

lithograph with collaged lithograph
Mimmo Paladino Hon RA
(edition of 25: £5,400 each)

550 THE RED WORKROOM £ 3,600

etching with watercolour, collage and pencil
Anthony Green RA

551 WELCOME TO STRETFORD MALL £ 485

monoprint
Eva Goldwyn-Simpkins

552 33 £ 2,350

woodcut
Katsutoshi Yuasa
(edition of 5: £1,950 each)

553 SEPTEMBER GARDEN £ 1,073

screenprint
Frederick Cuming RA
(edition of 75: £900 each)

554 STUDIO, EVENING MOONRISE £ 1,223

screenprint
Frederick Cuming RA
(edition of 75: £1,020 each)

555 UNLOCKING CEZANNE'S PLANES £ 675

screenprint with drawing
Jenny Wiener
(edition of 15: £575 each)

556 SWING £ 675

screenprint with drawing
Jenny Wiener
(edition of 15: £575 each)

557 THE DRESSER £ 650
collograph and watercolour
Vicky Oldfield
(edition of 30: £520 each)

558 ROAREIM – FLANNAN £ 500
etching
Norman Ackroyd RA
(edition of 90: £400 each)

559 BRANCASTER MORNING £ 500
etching
Norman Ackroyd RA
(edition of 90: £400 each)

560 KINLOCHBERVIE £ 450
etching
Norman Ackroyd RA
(edition of 90: £350 each)

561 ORANMORE REVISITED £ 650
etching
Norman Ackroyd RA
(edition of 90: £500 each)

562 CARTMEL IN FEBRUARY AND WINDERMERE £ 950
etching
Norman Ackroyd RA
(edition of 90: £750 each)

563 FLANNAN ISLANDS £ 950
etching
Norman Ackroyd RA
(edition of 90: £750 each)

564 PRIDE (FROM: SEVEN DEADLY SINS) £ 5,070
screenprint
Michael Craig-Martin RA
(edition of 30: £3,900 each)

565 GLOBALISATION £ 2,810
inkjet on hahnemule photo rag paper
Michael Craig-Martin RA
(edition of 40: £1,920 each)

566 STUDY FOR GLOBE 2 £ 2,600
inkjet
Michael Craig-Martin RA

567 STUDY FOR PAINTING (TOXIC) £ 2,880
inkjet
Michael Craig-Martin RA

568 HEAD II £ 700
inkjet and relief
Paul Coldwell
(edition of 3: £600 each)

569 SEX SYDNEY £ 570
polymer gravure
Tracey Emin RA
(edition of 100: £400 each)

570 SMALL AND BEAUTIFUL £ 450
polymer gravure
Tracey Emin RA
(edition of 300: £275 each)

571 CLOUDY ISLAND £ 500
etching
Sir Nicholas Grimshaw RA
(edition of 12: £350 each)

572 SEX SYDNEY III £ 570
polymer gravure
Tracey Emin RA
(edition of 100: £400 each)

573 TOWER OF BABEL: FIRE: LIBRARY OF BABYLON £ 700
digital print on Somerset paper
Jackie Parry
(edition of 20: £600 each)

574 MOONLIT WOODS £ 790
woodcut
Tom Hammick
(edition of 25: £600 each)

575 GOAT GIRL £ 21,600
unique hand-coloured etching
Paula Rego

576 GUARDIANS £ 21,600
unique hand-coloured etching
Paula Rego

577 UNTITLED (WORKSHOP) £ 700
digital print
Sophie Michael
(edition of 10: £500 each)

578 KLEINES SEESTÜCK IV £ 2,660
woodcut on japanese shiragiku paper
Christiane Baumgartner
(edition of 18: £2,220 each)

579 THE MOON IS DOWN £ 1,430
sceenprint
Stephen Chambers RA
(edition of 30: £1,188 each)

580 THE ACT OF RHETORIC £ 1,350
screenprint
Stephen Chambers RA
(edition of 30: £1,098 each)

581 THE ACT OF WAR £ 1,350
screenprint
Stephen Chambers RA
(edition of 30: £1,098 each)

582 HANG ON A MINUTE LADS, I'VE GOT A GREAT IDEA £ 1,000
archival print
Richard Wilson RA
(edition of 30: £800 each)

583 WHEN HOPE IS BURNING £ 490
mezzotint
Stuart Duffin
(edition of 30: £420 each)

584 ETERNAL GAZE (LEFT): WAVES £ 990

woodcut print
Nana Shiomi
(edition of 30: £740 each)

585 ETERNAL GAZE (RIGHT): MOUNTAINS £ 990

woodcut print
Nana Shiomi
(edition of 30: £740 each)

586 WHERE THE SIDEWALK ENDS £ 3,735

woodcut on japanese unryushi paper
Lisa Ruyter
(edition of 40: £2,880 each)

587 HEAD £ 3,100

etching
Tony Bevan RA
(edition of 12: £2,700 each)

588 WOODBLOCK INLAY 5 £ 2,490

woodcut
Richard Woods
(edition of 45: £1,920 each)

589 ELENA AND CRESSIE GET READY FOR £ 5,400
THE PARTY 4

screenprint on persex with inkjet background
Julian Opie
(edition of 30: £5,400 each)

590 LANDSCAPE 17 £ 3,600

sugar-lift aquatint and hand painting
Paul Winstanley

591 32 £ 2,350

woodcut
Katsutoshi Yuasa
(edition of 5: £1,950 each)

592 HEAD £ 4,100

etching
Tony Bevan RA
(edition of 12: £3,600 each)

593 SAFETY LAST £ 9,000
series of 8 etchings
Catherine Yass
(edition of 20: £6,300 each)

594 PROMENADE, ROCKEFELLER SKATERS £ 1,100
etching and aquatint
Bill Jacklin RA
(edition of 50: £900 each)

595 SHRINE WINDOW NO.1 £ 1,200
collotype
Akiko Takizawa
(edition of 10: £1,000 each)

596 STAR SPANGLED #2 £ 6,160
sugarlift aquatint, carborundum and handpainting
Gillian Ayres RA

597 RESISTANCE / ACCEPTANCE £ 520
CGI
Stuart Duffin
(edition of 30: £450 each)

598 A HUMUMENT P73 : HERE WAS A WOMAN £ 395
epson and screenprint
Tom Phillips RA
(edition of 75: £300 each)

599 A HUMUMENT P168 : TWILIGHT RAILINGS £ 395
epson and screenprint
Tom Phillips RA
(edition of 75: £300 each)

600 LOLITA £ 900
epson and screenprint
Tom Phillips RA
(edition of 75: £750 each)

601 AFTER HENRY JAMES £ 950
epson and screenprint
Tom Phillips RA
(edition of 75: £800 each)

602 COILED SERPENT £ 375
relief print on antique paper
Lauren Drescher
(edition of 15: £300 each)

603 LONG SERPENT £ 375
relief print on antique paper
Lauren Drescher
(edition of 15: £300 each)

604 IN THE EVENING £ 600
etching
Meike Georgi
(edition of 10: £550 each)

605 GIANT STEPS £ 768
silkscreen print
Trevor Sutton
(edition of 20: £600 each)

606 CYPRESS TREE £ 3,600
etching
Alaleh Alamir
(edition of 20: £3,600 each)

607 VIRTUE £ 1,150
lithograph
Christopher Le Brun PRA
(edition of 35: £960 each)

608 SABINE GROUP (AFTER GIAMBOLOGNA) •
bronze
Ivor Abrahams RA

* Refer to Sales Desk

609 IN THERE, SOMEWHERE   £ 140
etching and aquatint
Lynn Saunders
(edition of 5: £120 each)

610 AUTUMN OAK   £ 395
soft-ground etching
Terry Kubecki
(edition of 50: £295 each)

611 THE PLANE   £ 875
photograph
John Pennicott
(edition of 10: £580 each)

612 UNTITLED 6   £ 420
monoprint
Belinda Ellis

613 UNTITLED: FROM THE SERIES "LIGHT"   £ 570
drypoint
Igor Shichkov

614 UNTITLED   £ 540
intaglio
Vera Boele-Keimer
(edition of 5: £480 each)

615 CHAIR FOR ONE   £ 200
etching
Viktorija Osipova
(edition of 15: £140 each)

616 A BREEZE CUTS A PAUSE   £ 4,060
sugar-lift aquatint and carborundum
Gillian Ayres RA
(edition of 15: £3,600 each)

617 PATHÉ NEWSREEL – TROOPS GOING INTO BELSEN – MEMORY NFS

monoprint
Gillian Kogan

618 PUFFIN ISLAND £ 350

etching and aquatint
Jason Hicklin
(edition of 30: £290 each)

619 ST TROPEZ £ 130

etching
Silke Schelenz
(edition of 25: £90 each)

620 STAIRCASE TO THE LIBRARY £ 390

etching
Richard Bawden
(edition of 85: £300 each)

621 COOLING TOWERS £ 300

linocut
Ashley Stark
(edition of 10: £200 each)

622 COKETOWN, NOVEMBER £ 250

aquatint
Peter Freeth RA
(edition of 20: £175 each)

623 WOULD YOU ADAM 'N' EVE IT? (STUDIES) £ 375

aquatint
Peter Freeth RA
(edition of 30: £300 each)

624 SHOPTALK ON PARNASSUS (MANET'S CAT, SEURAT'S DOG, PIERO'S MAGPIE) £ 400

aquatint
Peter Freeth RA
(edition of 40: £325 each)

625 WHAT THE HAMMER, WHAT THE CHAIN?   £ 650
(REBUILDING JERUSALEM)
aquatint
Peter Freeth RA
(edition of 30: £550 each)

626 FRONTIERS   £ 575
aquatint
Peter Freeth RA
(edition of 20: £500 each)

627 ON LINE IX   £ 450
etching
Vanessa Jackson
(edition of 20: £360 each)

628 ON LINE VIII   £ 450
etching
Vanessa Jackson
(edition of 20: £360 each)

629 SHINING   £ 575
woodcut
Sara Lee
(edition of 25: £425 each)

630 TOGETHER   £ 650
etching
Barton Hargreaves
(edition of 27: £450 each)

631 SUNSET AT CADIZ   £ 375
etching
Paul Hawdon
(edition of 40: £325 each)

632 OVER THE WALL   £ 575
aquatint
Peter Freeth RA
(edition of 20: £500 each)

633 THE LIBRARY OF DR LONDON   £ 3,400
hand-coloured lithograph
Adam Dant
(edition of 15: £3,000 each)

634 IT WAS A DEVICE £ 1,250

three-plate polymer gravure

Glen Baxter

(edition of 50: £950 each)

635 STRIDING OUT £ 620

woodcut etching

Simon Lawson

(edition of 35: £460 each)

636 FERALIS £ 795

archival digital print

Suzanne Moxhay

(edition of 10: £595 each)

637 JONO'S LOBSTER £ 975

digital and oil

Evi Antonio

(edition of 10: £475 each)

638 STONES OF VENICE SANTA MARIA £ 2,500
DELLA VISITAZIONE, VENEZIA

carborundum and screenprint

Joe Tilson RA

(edition of 25: £1,800 each)

639 STONES OF VENICE SAN TROUASO, VENEZIA £ 2,500

carborundum and screenprint

Joe Tilson RA

(edition of 25: £1,800 each)

640 STONES OF VENICE SAN PANTALON, VENEZIA £ 2,500

carborundum and screenprint

Joe Tilson RA

(edition of 25: £1,800 each)

641 OLYMPIC AQUATICS CENTRE IN CONSTRUCTION £ 320

wood engraving

Anne Desmet RA

(edition of 50: £200 each)

642 OLYMPIC SHADOWS £ 320

wood engraving

Anne Desmet RA

(edition of 100: £200 each)

643 LONDON OLYMPIC SITE – WWII ARCHAEOLOGY £ 320
wood engraving
Anne Desmet RA
(edition of 30: £200 each)

644 LONDON OLYMPIC VELODROME £ 320
wood engraving
Anne Desmet RA
(edition of 50: £200 each)

645 DAYS OF UNCERTAINTY £ 3,250
wood engraving and gold leaf collaged onto linoprint
Anne Desmet RA

646 NINE CLEMENTINES £ 650
woodcut
Hilary Daltry
(edition of 50: £550 each)

647 FOREIGN LAND £ 495
woodcut
Sara Lee
(edition of 25: £375 each)

648 ATHNE £ 850
archival digital print
Suzanne Moxhay
(edition of 10: £695 each)

649 BAREFOOT DUET £ 720
woodcut
Eileen Cooper RA
(edition of 40: £600 each)

650 MARTHA'S RADIO £ 350
etching
Rob White
(edition of 35: £250 each)

651 UNDER LAVENDER SKIES £ 775
linocut
Eileen Cooper RA
(edition of 40: £650 each)

652 BLUE BOY £ 2,200
monoprint
Eileen Cooper RA

653 LILAC NIGHT £ 775
linocut
Eileen Cooper RA
(edition of 40: £650 each)

654 TIME AND IDENTITY (III) £ 660
aquatint
Michael Sandle RA
(edition of 30: £600 each)

655 TIME AND IDENTITY (BRIDGEHEAD) (II) £ 660
aquatint
Michael Sandle RA
(edition of 30: £600 each)

656 TIME AND IDENTITY (I) £ 660
aquatint
Michael Sandle RA
(edition of 30: £600 each)

657 ALDEBURGH £ 675
etching
Derek Chambers
(edition of 75: £595 each)

658 HAPPY, ALL SMILES £ 410
screenprint
Adam Bridgland
(edition of 40: £300 each)

659 SUNFLOWERS £ 7,415
lithograph
Jim Dine
(edition of 17: £6,900 each)

660 CYCLONE £ 990
silkscreen with diamond dust
Dan Baldwin
(edition of 75: £990 each)

661 CARNATIONS £ 2,040
inkjet print
Leonard McComb RA
(edition of 50: £1,950 each)

662 VERDANT FIELD I £ 1,260
colour carburundum
Hughie O'Donoghue RA
(edition of 25: £1,020 each)

663 VERDANT FIELD II £ 1,260
colour carburundum
Hughie O'Donoghue RA
(edition of 25: £1,020 each)

664 POTTERY AND PORTUGUESE TILES £ 795
etching and watercolour
Meg Dutton
(edition of 50: £700 each)

665 BOGNOR BABY £ 1,050
print and collage
Charlotte Cory
(edition of 100: £1,000 each)

666 BY THE THAMES £ 375
woodcut
Sasa Marinkov
(edition of 30: £295 each)

667 MARGE £ 850
screenprint
Brendan Neiland
(edition of 20: £600 each)

668 DIFFERENTIAL SPACE £ 350
montage
Fiona Marianne Bennett
(edition of 5: £260 each)

669 OUTBACK £ 975
photograph
Jean Macalpine
(edition of 10: £875 each)

670 BLOCK 2 £ 740

screenprint and graphite powder
George Charman
(edition of 5: £650 each)

671 NORTH TRURO £ 920

screenprint
John Mackechnie
(edition of 25: £800 each)

672 PEACHES FROM THE SOUTH £ 2,040

inkjet print
Leonard McComb RA
(edition of 50: £1,950 each)

673 MELONS FROM THE SOUTH £ 2,040

inkjet print
Leonard McComb RA
(edition of 50: £1,950 each)

674 LEYLANDII £ 465

etching
Dolores de Sade
(edition of 20: £380 each)

675 HUMPBACK WHALE II £ 750

etching
Marion Macphee
(edition of 20: £650 each)

676 QUIET AFTER RAIN £ 1,350

etching and monoprint
Morgan Doyle

677 ORANGES FROM THE SOUTH £ 2,040

inkjet print
Leonard McComb RA
(edition of 50: £1,950 each)

678 EIGHTH ENCOUNTER I £ 950

lithograph
Jasia Szerszynska
(edition of 50: £750 each)

679 SIX IDENTICAL SHAPES 82° £ 350
serigraph
John Carter RA
(edition of 40: £260 each)

680 BALLOON CARRYING BIRD £ 1,800
woodcut
Aithan Shapira
(edition of 6: £1,500 each)

681 NOT, OUR, TYPE, DARLING £ 900
digital print with screenprint glazes
Brad Faine
(edition of 50: £700 each)

682 VEGAS II £ 4,800
c-type print
David Clerihew
(edition of 10: £3,600 each)

683 AZURE BLUE ETCHING £ 3,380
etching with chine collé
Ian Davenport
(edition of 30: £2,880 each)

684 SHADOW £ 1,130
screenprint
Tess Jaray RA
(edition of 40: £900 each)

685 NEBRASKA III £ 1,350
screenprint
Albert Irvin RA
(edition of 35: £1,080 each)

686 NEBRASKA V £ 1,350
screenprint and woodblock
Albert Irvin RA
(edition of 35: £1,080 each)

687 UNTITLED £ 450
etching
Tooney Phillips
(edition of 10: £400 each)

688 UNFOLDING PLANES IN YELLOW £ 590
relief print and blind embossing
John Carter RA
(edition of 12: £520 each)

689 PERFECT CHEMISTRY £ 520
giclée print
Richard Kirwan
(edition of 30: £450 each)

690 FLYING GEESE £ 225
screenprint
Lucy Gough
(edition of 50: £125 each)

691 EIGHT IDENTICAL SHAPES 82° £ 350
screenprint
John Carter RA
(edition of 40: £260 each)

692 SEVENTH ENCOUNTER I £ 950
lithograph
Jasia Szerszynska
(edition of 50: £750 each)

693 LOUIS £ 410
etching
Helen Fay
(edition of 65: £355 each)

694 THREE-LEGGED RACE £ 100
relief print
Sharon Low
(edition of 30: £60 each)

695 CRANEFLY II £ 200
etching
Sarah Pirkis
(edition of 75: £160 each)

696 HOW STILL IT IS… £ 135
wood engraving
Sue Cave
(edition of 50: £95 each)

697 SUNLIGHT THROUGH REDWOODS £ 300
linocut
Alexandra Olding
(edition of 8: £250 each)

698 ON THE ICKNIELD WAY NO. 4 £ 145
drypoint
Hilary Hanley
(edition of 10: £120 each)

699 THE COB £ 150
drypoint
Glenna Devlin
(edition of 20: £110 each)

700 MARY AND THE GUARDSMAN £ 225
linocut
Michael Evans
(edition of 75: £180 each)

701 INSECT CIRCUS £ 180
etching
Caro Halford
(edition of 5: £90 each)

702 AUSTERITY MEASURE £ 320
screenprint
Henningham Family Press
(edition of 50: £180 each)

703 ATLANTIC LOW II £ 550
hand-coloured digital pigment print
Murray Robertson
(edition of 20: £480 each)

704 BACCHANAL LIVE £ 170
etching
Mike Tingle
(edition of 50: £110 each)

705 GOLDCREST £ 279
drypoint and watercolour
Richard Spare
(edition of 100: £199 each)

706 PAPER ROUND NO. 2, FROM UNREMARKABLE STORIES £ 200

c-type print
Rob Ball
(edition of 10: £140 each)

707 EARLY STORM £ 240

etching
David L Carpanini
(edition of 50: £185 each)

708 WELSH HILL FARM £ 245

wood engraving
Howard Phipps
(edition of 150: £185 each)

709 ON TIME £ 120

wood engraving
Rebecca Coleman
(edition of 30: £85 each)

710 THE PREDATORS £ 140

etching wih aquatint
Martin Ridgwell
(edition of 30: £100 each)

711 A GRÉVY'S ZEBRA £ 500

linocut
Margaret Ann Sadler
(edition of 2: £400 each)

712 THE BLACK VASE £ 295

relief / linocut
Caroline Isgar
(edition of 20: £245 each)

713 THE DARK AND MARVELLOUS ROOM £ 295

monoprint
Caroline Isgar

714 CAT IN A BOX £ 145

etching
Theresa Pateman
(edition of 110: £120 each)

715 CHILCOMBE £ 245
wood engraving
Howard Phipps
(edition of 150: £185 each)

716 HUG £ 336
wood engraving
David Frazer
(edition of 60: £336 each)

717 TOWER BRIDGE £ 195
etching
Joseph Winkelman
(edition of 150: £150 each)

718 UNTITLED £ 585
etching
Tracey Richardson
(edition of 25: £425 each)

719 HOME ALONE, SOUTH YORKSHIRE £ 95
collograph with drypoint
Emily Thomas
(edition of 20: £70 each)

720 100 RUNNING LINES HYDE PARK £ 325
etching
Marianne Nix
(edition of 90: £225 each)

721 AFTER THE SNOW £ 240
etching
Rachel Grigor
(edition of 20: £186 each)

722 AFTER DARK £ 660
screenprint with woodblock
Anita Klein
(edition of 35: £480 each)

723 WHITLINGHAM MARSH – SNOW £ 250
etching
Ivy Smith
(edition of 20: £180 each)

724 FUCHSIA £ 260
etching
Sharda Mehta
(edition of 30: £230 each)

725 PAUL SMITH LONDON III £ 195
etching
Oscar Whicheloe
(edition of 30: £140 each)

726 CHOPPERS £ 230
etching
Tamsin Relly
(edition of 20: £160 each)

727 THE BUTCHER'S DOG £ 550
etching with watercolour
Eric Vande Pitte
(edition of 8: £325 each)

728 GEOMETRIC HEARTS £ 5,000
etching with watercolour
Bella Easton
(edition of 10: £5,000 each - only available framed)

729 DOG SUIT £ 240
etching
Chris Salmon
(edition of 100: £195 each)

730 HERE I COME... £ 365
drypoint chine collé
Basia Lautman
(edition of 32: £295 each)

731 IT'S A DOGE'S LIFE ON THE GRAND CANAL £ 2,680
etching
Graham Clarke
(edition of 400: £2,500 each)

732 VISITOR £ 650
woodcut print on kozo
Trevor Banthorpe
(edition of 5: £575 each)

733 STUDY FOR A CHAISE LONGUE AFTER LECADRE   £ 350

etching
Ian Ritchie RA
(edition of 15: £250 each)

---

734 WING - BRUSHED   £ 1,950

monoprint
Phillip King RA

---

735 CYCLIST   £ 375

etching
Adrian Bartlett
(edition of 75: £350 each)

---

736 THE TELEPHONE   £ 300

four-block linoprint
Steven Hubbard
(edition of 50: £250 each)

---

737 THE BOROUGH   £ 1,375

letterpress print
Alan Kitching
(edition of 45: £1,045 each)

---

738 THE MEN'S GROUP   £ 800

etching
Freya Payne
(edition of 15: £650 each)

---

739 WATERLOO STATION   £ 400

linocut
Manuel Roman
(edition of 8: £300 each)

---

740 WITH THE BRUSHES   £ 400

digital print
Mark Hampson
(edition of 60: £350 each)

---

741 TESLA   £ 380

etching
Biljana Tesic
(edition of 20: £350 each)

742 LOST AND FOUND, KINGS CROSS ST PANCRAS   £ 549
lithograph with hand colouring
Lucy Kristiane Farley
(edition of 20: £435 each)

743 WOMAN UNDER RED VEIL   £ 880
archival digital print
Guler Ates
(edition of 15: £650 each)

744 H5   £ 460
etching with hand colouring
Danny Rolph
(edition of 40: £300 each)

745 THE LONG VIEW, REFLECTED   £ 1,650
drypoint
Chris Orr RA
(edition of 20: £1,450 each)

746 SAVOY EXTERNAL LETTERING IN SAVOY GRILL,   £ 880
THE SAVOY, JUNE 2009
photograph
Siobhan Doran
(edition of 9: £780 each)

747 PICCADILLY CIRCUS   £ 295
linoprint
Mick Armson
(edition of 75: £195 each)

748 GOING HOME   £ 160
woodcut
Martin Saull
(edition of 40: £130 each)

749 TWEET   £ 80
woodcut and watercolour
Besheer Abbaro
(edition of 110: £35 each)

750 BEAUTIFUL BRUTALISM   £ 90
photograph
Joanne Underhill
(edition of 100: £40 each)

751 LONDON FROM PRIMROSE HILL £ 625
etching
John Duffin
(edition of 150: £550 each)

752 STREET ENTERTAINERS, COVENT GARDEN £ 350
etching
Toni Martina
(edition of 70: £290 each)

753 REQUIEM £ 950
coloured pencil and pen
Elizabeth Collini

754 TUNNEL VISION £ 590
etching
Martin Langford
(edition of 100: £450 each)

755 MAPPA MUNDI LONDON £ 900
thermal ribbon on vinyl
Ewan Eason
(edition of 150: £750 each)

756 REGENT STREET RAIN £ 350
etching
John Duffin
(edition of 150: £295 each)

757 AND DID THOSE FEET IN ANCIENT TIME, LONDON 2012 £ 680
copperplate etching
David Borrington
(edition of 35: £500 each)

758 TOGETHER 3 £ 975
archival digital print
Barton Hargreaves
(edition of 25: £725 each)

759 BUILDING THE SHARD OF GLASS – FROM BACK OF LONDON BRIDGE STATION £ 300
etching
Jeanette Barnes
(edition of 30: £240 each)

760 LAUNDRETTE £ 800
etching with hand colouring
Sophie Layton
(edition of 15: £650 each)

761 REMEMBER ME £ 320
linocut
Gail Brodholt
(edition of 75: £250 each)

762 RETAIL THERAPY £ 320
linocut
Gail Brodholt
(edition of 75: £250 each)

763 BABEL £ 870
etching
Nikolai Batakov
(edition of 30: £800 each)

764 HOXTON SQUARE £ 670
hand-coloured lithograph
Adam Dant
(edition of 60: £550 each)

765 DOWN CHARING CROSS ROAD £ 525
pencil
Timothy Hyman RA

766 SOUND OF MUSIC IN SUBURBIA £ 560
linocut and etching
Catherine Sutcliffe-Fuller
(edition of 20: £495 each)

767 THE VISIT £ 400
etching with aquatint
Sonia Martin
(edition of 20: £350 each)

768 ROYAL PALACE OF WHITEHALL: £ 440
'ANGELS OF LONDON' SERIES
two-plate mixed media etching
Giulia Zaniol
(edition of 45: £385 each)

769 THAMES BARRIER £ 350
etching with aquatint
Nicholas Richards
(edition of 50: £275 each)

770 LONDON LIFE I £ 220
multiblock linocut and lead type
Sally Cutler
(edition of 50: £195 each)

771 OLYMPICDOM 2012 £ 250
screenprint
Frank Kiely
(edition of 150: £150 each)

772 COME FOR A STROLL ON THE PIER £ 219
linoprint
Stephen Gibbs
(edition of 69: £169 each)

773 PRELUDE £ 400
etching with aquatint
Sonia Martin
(edition of 20: £350 each)

774 BLUE TILE £ 370
etching and block print
Katherine Jones
(edition of 25: £300 each)

775 INTERIOR £ 270
etching
David Lintine
(edition of 35: £230 each)

776 EKHO RADIO £ 480
reduction linocut
Helen Peyton
(edition of 15: £420 each

777 THE RITZ £ 185
dry writing, print
Gillian Westgate
(edition of 30: £145 each)

778 IL DUOMO – ORVIETO £ 195

etching

Paul Hawdon

(edition of 40: £165 each)

779 DERWENT WATER II £ 425

drypoint

Melvyn Petterson

(edition of 30: £325 each)

780 TOBY £ 1,160

etching

Dame Elizabeth Blackadder RA

(edition of 50: £960 each)

781 LA TUILERIE £ 1,170

etching

Dame Elizabeth Blackadder RA

(edition of 80: £1,020 each)

782 GLADIOLI £ 2,410

screenprint

Dame Elizabeth Blackadder RA

(edition of 80: £2,160 each)

783 TAYLORVILLE £ 620

hand-coloured etching

Bronwen Sleigh

(edition of 20: £500 each)

784 APPROACHING STORM £ 220

aquatint

Ruth de Monchaux

(edition of 40: £150 each)

785 PINETREES £ 215

aquatint

Ruth de Monchaux

(edition of 40: £145 each)

786 HAFNARBRAUT £ 620

hand-coloured etching

Bronwen Sleigh

(edition of 20: £500 each)

787 BLUE HOLD   £ 1,100
nine-plate colour lithograph
Elizabeth Magill
(edition of 75: £850 each)

788 WATER SONG: I (PATIO DE L'ACEQUIA, GENERALIFE)   £ 550
archival inkjet and watercolour print
Jennifer Dickson RA
(edition of 20: £350 each)

789 VANISHING POINT (MOTTISFONT ABBEY)   £ 350
archival inkjet and watercolour print
Jennifer Dickson RA
(edition of 40: £250 each)

790 MORNING LIGHT (MONASTERIO DE PEDRALBES, BARCELONA)   £ 525
archival inkjet and watercolour print
Jennifer Dickson RA
(edition of 20: £325 each)

791 HYDRANGEA WALK (ISOLA BELLA)   £ 625
archival inkjet and watercolour print
Jennifer Dickson RA
(edition of 20: £425 each)

792 VOYAGE   £ 975
photograph
Jean Macalpine
(edition of 10: £875 each)

793 WATER SONG: II (RIVER HIRAETHLIN, BODNANT)   £ 575
archival inkjet and watercolour print
Jennifer Dickson RA
(edition of 20: £375 each)

794 HOMAGE TO RUSSELL PAGE (LONGLEAT)   £ 350
archival inkjet and watercolour print
Jennifer Dickson RA
(edition of 40: £250 each)

795 ALL THE THINGS WE LEFT UNSAID £ 350
(A BOOK ABOUT WORDS WITHOUT WORDS) VOL. 2
thread-ink and digital print (artist's book)
Joan Beadle

796 PENANCE £ 195
hand-rolled scrolls, lithograph on Bible paper (artist's book)
Bea Denton
(edition of 50: £195 each)

797 EROSION £ 750
artist's book
Jean Woods
(edition of 4: £750 each)

798 NOT GOD, NOT TREASURE, NOT YOU £ 1,000
artist's book
Sioban Piercy

799 GEBURAH AND BINAH £ 280
screenprint (artist's book)
Paolo Carraro
(edition of 12: £280 each)

800 GEGHANOOSH'S BIRTH CERTIFICATE £ 300
mixed media (artist's book)
Batool Showghi
(edition of 7: £300 each)

801 TEMPTATION £ 120
fruit papyrus book (artist's book)
Dizzy Pragnell
(edition of 10: £120 each)

802 WITH THE WORMS £ 100
screenprint (artist's book)
John Dilnot
(edition of 300: £100 each)

803 A QUICK BROWN FOX NFS
letterpress print (artist's book)
Vanessa Vargo

804 ADDRESS AND TELEPHONE – A COLLECTION   £ 260
OF POEMS FROM AN OLD ADDRESS BOOK
copperplate (artist's book)
Victoria Thornburn

805 PLOT 82   Editions available for sale
letterpress, lithograph, digital print; hand bound (artist's book)
Evy Jokhova
(edition of 30: £125 each)

806 MARTIN'S PREMIUM CORNED BEEF   £ 45
relief print on paper and card (artist's book)
Ruth Martin
(edition of 50: £45 each)

807 DNA FEMALE DNA MALE, NO. 3   £ 350
lasercut pergamenata paper, nylon thread (artist's book)
Christine Pereira-Adams
(edition of 46: £350 each)

808 KING OF COLANDERS   £ 1,270
etching (artist's book)
Marcelle Hanselaar
(edition of 7: £1,270 each)

809 SOUL OF THE MINE, WOODWOSE BOOK   £ 5,000
leather and paper (artist's book)
Tom O'Reilly

Large Weston Room

810 SWEETLY THE AIR FLEW OVERHEAD, BATTLE WITH THE UNICORNS NO. 11 £ 33,000
paper, copper, brass, elastoplast, feathers, silk and paint
Cathy de Monchaux

811 KURUNA £ 7,000
oil
Andrea McLean

812 LIBRA £ 9,000
inkjet print
Tim Head

813 LIBRA 2 £ 9,000
inkjet print
Tim Head

814 A LAMENT £ 54,000
white aluminium shelf with thrown porcelain vessels in white glazes
Edmund de Waal

815 THAT HAGEN GIRL £ 6,500
acrylic
Simon Hiscock

816 BRONTËAN ABSTRACT (DELETIONS FROM THE ORIGINAL MANUSCRIPT OF JANE EYRE) £ 21,600
c-type colour prints (set of 12)
Cornelia Parker RA

817 UNTITLED #05 NFS
pencil and coloured pencil
Tomma Abts

818 SELF PORTRAITS AS WOMAN WITH   *
BANDAGED FACE
c-type print
Gillian Wearing RA

819 DIRTY (WHITE) 7 £ 24,000
oil and acrylic on aluminium
Angela de la Cruz

820 IN THE HOUSE OF £ 8,000
digital 3D colour print
Tom Lomax
(edition of 15: £8,000 each)

821 BRONTËAN ABSTRACT £ 4,200
(EMILY BRONTË'S BLOTTING PAPER)
c-type colour print of scan
Cornelia Parker RA

822 BRONTËAN ABSTRACT £ 4,200
(ANNE BRONTË'S NEEDLE)
silver gelatin print of an SEM image
Cornelia Parker RA

823 BRONTËAN ABSTRACT £ 4,200
(PINHOLE MADE BY CHARLOTTE BRONTË)
silver gelatin print of an SEM image
Cornelia Parker RA

824 SAMSON NFS
oil, acrylic, steel, pastel and charcoal
Anselm Kiefer Hon RA

825 RED WITH SHADOW £ 7,000
red oxide pigment on panel and wall
Onya McCausland

826 FIELD, RED WITH 5 LINES £ 12,000
cut-out
Tess Jaray RA

* Refer to Sales Desk

827 FIELD, RED BEND £ 12,000
cut-out
Tess Jaray RA

828 TABITHA II £ 4,000
oil on wood and silk
Jane Bustin

829 BELOVED IV £ 4,000
ink and paper on oak
Jane Bustin

830 TWO POPLARS NFS
oil on board
Patrick George

831 GREENGAGE TREE IN THE MIDDLE £ 15,000
oil on board
Patrick George

832 SHED £ 15,000
oil
Humphrey Ocean RA

833 SWERVE £ 10,000
oil
Humphrey Ocean RA

834 SHIP £ 12,000
oil
Humphrey Ocean RA

835 PEG PAINTING £ 40,000
watercolour and wooden pegs
Annie Morris

836 FLOOD £ 300,000
blue pencil with black and white aquacryl
and aluminium
Shirazeh Houshiary

837 ARC £ 30,000
swaledale fossil limestone
Paul de Monchaux

838 SEA LILY £ 30,000
swaledale fossil limestone
Paul de Monchaux

839 A PLINTH FROM A GALLERY IN LAHORE £ 16,000
UV inkjet print on aluminium
Rashid Rana
(edition of 5: £16,000 each)

840 CHICKEN CHAIR £ 1,300
animal bones
Olu Shobowale

Small
Weston Room

841 **SELF PORTRAIT 2**   *
black and white fibre based silver gelatin print
Jayne Parker
(edition of 5)

842 **TRILOGY: KETTLE'S YARD**   *
digibeta from original 16mm film
Jayne Parker

* Refer to Sales Desk

843 RED AND UNREAD NFS
oil on board
John Byrne

844 FAT MAN'S HERBAL CURES, OPUS 0.1777 £ 16,000
oil
Alan Davie

845 STILL LIFE WITH FAN £ 40,000
oil
Dame Elizabeth Blackadder RA

846 NIGHT SWIMMING I £ 5,900
colour carburundum
Hughie O'Donoghue RA
(edition of 5: £4,800 each)

847 CUT GROUND GREY RED NFS
oil on aluminium
Sean Scully

**848 PURE TO ANOTHER
(PORTRAIT OF BRIAN KENNEDY)** £ 20,000
oil on linen
Colin Davidson

849 ANCIENT MARINER £ 15,000
oil
John Bellany RA

850 AFFERENT SEA £ 3,000
oil on linen
Eddie Kennedy

851 TURVILLE S FOUNTAIN £ 350
etching
Ian Ritchie RA
(edition of 15: £250 each)

852 RAASAY THOUGHTS £ 350
etching
Ian Ritchie RA
(edition of 15: £250 each)

853 WATERSIDE, MELLERSTAIN £5,000
oil on board
Calum McClure

854 THE CLEARING, INVERMAY £2,000
oil on board
Calum McClure

855 STUDY OF GLEN HANSARD £ 2,900
oil on linen
Colin Davidson

856 TURVILLE S FOUNTAIN CLOSE UP £ 350
etching
Ian Ritchie RA
(edition of 15: £250 each)

857 THINGS TO COME NO. 11 £ 4,500
oil on linen
Keith Wilson

858 HOTEL BEDROOM £ 8,000
oil
Euan Gray

859 SASH £ 30,000
oil
Alison Watt

860 DEW POINT £ 1,400
acrylic
Marian Leven

861 ANDVORD BAY, ANTARCTICA £ 30,000
oil on wood panel (triptych)
Frances Walker

862 VULCANO NFS
oil
Hughie O'Donoghue RA

863 DORIC GREY NFS
oil on linen
Sean Scully

864 SCHEMATIC SKATE £ 15,000
mixed media on board
Will Maclean

865 DARK YESNABY £ 48,000
mixed media
Barbara Rae RA

866 SUN LOUNGERS £ 1,500
ink and acrylic on board
Euan Gray

867 WALL – ORGIVA £ 8,000
mixed media
Barbara Rae RA

868 CITY £ 550
photograph
Norman Mcbeath
(edition of 35: £450 each)

869 PORTRAIT OF SIR TERRY FROST NFS
oil
Neil Shawcross

870 UNTITLED NO. 33 £ 66,000
oil
Callum Innes

871 BLACK STAR NFS
oil
Alison Watt

872 FEAR-BATA / THE BOATMAN £ 24,000
mixed media on board
Will Maclean

873 FLUX £ 5,000
acrylic
Marian Leven

874	**BUFFALO GRILL**	£ 37,500
	oil	
	Jock McFadyen	
875	**LITTLE JAIN STUDY, OPUS 0.1090**	£ 5,000
	oil on board	
	Alan Davie	
876	**THE DANDY**	£ 3,200
	mixed media	
	John Byrne	
877	**ISLINGTON INTERIOR**	£ 6,500
	oil	
	Jock McFadyen	
878	**DAVID (NO. 3 OF 8)**	£ 19,800
	live matches	
	David Mach RA	
879	**GLASGOW SCHOOL OF ART**	NFS
	cardboard	
	Gordon Benson RA	
880	**THE UNKNOWN**	£ 20,000
	resin, perspex and paint	
	Kenny Hunter	
881	**MONUMENT TO A MOUSE**	£ 2,000
	jesmonite and paint	
	Kenny Hunter	
	(edition of 15: £2,000 each)	

882 SUMMER GARDEN £ 20,000
oil
Anthony Eyton RA

883 MY FIRST ORCHID £ 8,000
oil
Olwyn Bowey RA

884 CHERRY BLOSSOM NEXT DOOR £ 18,000
oil
Anthony Eyton RA

885 TOWARDS THE END OF WINTER £ 15,000
oil
Carey Clarke

886 WESTMINSTER FROM THE MILLBANK TOWER £ 2,900
monotype
Peter Spens

887 ZURICH £ 12,500
oil
Ken Howard RA

888 FIGURES ON STEPS (VILLENEUVETTE) £ 2,500
pencil, mixed media, crayon, acrylic and ink
Ivor Abrahams RA

889 SKELLIG £ 2,500
oil
Neal Greig

890 NORTH ROAD II £ 2,500
oil
Patricia Burns

891 GET WELL AND STAR CHART:　　　£ 3,400
JANUARY MORNING
oil
Marilyn Hallam

892 BLACK ALDERS　　　£ 6,000
oil on linen
Sarah Gillespie

893 MOUTH VII, NEAR SHANGHAI　　　£ 10,500
chromogenic colour print
Nadav Kander
(edition of 5 *)

894 CHURCH OF THE TRANSFIGURATION (1781),　　　£ 750
TURCHASOVO, ARCHANGEL REGION
digital print
Richard Davies
(edition of 25: £600 each)

895 CHURCH OF THE VIRGIN HODIGITRA (1763),　　　£ 750
KIMZHA, ARCHANGEL REGION
digital print
Richard Davies
(edition of 25: £600 each)

896 RADIATE　　　£ 8,750
pastel
Matthew Draper

897 SPOTTY HOUSE, TIREE HEBRIDES, SCOTLAND　　　£ 1,650
acrylic
David Humphreys

898 REINFORCED CONCRETE I　　　£ 150
photograph
Alison Fenn
(edition of 10: £100 each)

899 TIVIDALE AQUEDUCT OVER THE NETHERTON　　　£ 220
TUNNEL BRANCH CANAL
relief print, linocut
Paul Hipkiss
(edition of 25: £180 each)

* Refer to Sales Desk

900 CHOICES £ 7,500
digital print from negative
Scott Mead
(edition of 5: £5,000 each)

901 MERE £ 1,750
etching and aquatint
Jason Hicklin
(edition of 30: £1,500 each)

902 TIDAL SURGE III £ 38,000
acrylic and collage
Anthony Whishaw RA

903 SUMMER TREESCAPE £ 20,000
acrylic
Anthony Whishaw RA

904 LONDON, TAKEN FROM ST PAULS £ 4,150
oil
Rob Shaw

905 BATTERSEA THROUGH THE WALL £ 9,500
photograph
Adrian Houston
(edition of 25: £6,000 each)

906 NEW YORK HOTEL ROOM £ 1,700
pastel
Richard Cartwright

907 YGGDRASIL £ 9,500
acrylic
Ian McKenzie Smith

908 WALKING DRAWINGS, £ 7,000
CUMBRIAN HEAVY HORSES I
lambda c-type print
Everton Wright
(edition of 7: £5,500 each)

909 DANCE WITH LOVE £ 6,500
oil
Guitty Khorsand

910 THE RAINBOW, TENNYSON DOWN £ 2,500
oil on panel
Frederick Cuming RA

911 DEMOLITION £ 7,000
oil on linen
Tim Parr

912 TRIPTYCH OF MODELS SHOWING NFS
DEVELOPMENT OF OLYMPIC SITE
card, acrylic, paint, timber and metal
Allies and Morrison Architects

913 PARADISE, NO. 3 NFS
oil
Selma Gurbuz

914 SUMMER ISLE £ 8,000
oil
Sarah Armstrong-Jones

915 REPRISE AND FALL: TALL TALES IN THE NFS
THAMES GATEWAY
wax, wood, aluminium and MDF
Unit 11, Greenwich University

916 THE UNDERDOG £ 1,500
oil pastel
Oliver Canti

917 CAMBRIDGE MOSQUE WALL DETAIL NFS
architectural model
Marks Barfield Architects

918 ORATORIAN CITY £ 1,500
pen
Luca Perricone

919 FREE PARKER PEN WITH EVERY INQUIRY NFS
hand-drawn back of envelope
Gihan Karunaratne

920 SIERRA ECHOES £ 2,200
oil
Yuichiro Kikuma

921 RED DRIFT, NO. 3	£ 9,000
oil	
Graham Crowley	

922 THE AYLESBURY TOWN HALL: PERSPECTIVE STUDY OF THE CANTEEN	£ 5,000
pigment pastel	
Hugh McEwen	

923 SOAR ALBA	£ 2,500
mixed media	
Eòghann MacColl	

924 ALL OUR VARIANT FUTURES II	£ 5,750
mixed wood construction	
Adam Melville	

925 ADAGIO	£ 18,000
acrylic	
Brendan Neiland	

926 SERIES 'GHIRLANDA CONTINUA': LUCE	£ 10,750
acrylic	
Jennifer Durrant RA	

927 MODERN DISCO (CHA, CHA, CHA) NO. 3	£ 1,500
mixed media	
Helena Ben-Zenou	

928 A SCHOOL OF ARCHITECTURE	£ 45,000
acrylic	
Will Alsop RA	

929 T.3.	£ 15,000
acrylic	
Gus Cummins RA	

930 BAPTISM AT WELL DRESSING	£ 950
acrylic	
Nelda Utilini	

931 FEEDING SOME MYTHS	£ 4,250
gouache and tempera	
Mick Rooney RA	

932 A MOMENT IN AVALON £ 4,250
gouache and tempera
Mick Rooney RA

933 THE DEVOTED GARDENER £ 3,500
oil and acrylic
Lee Madgwick

934 CITY PLACE £ 3,500
acrylic
Chris Wilkinson RA

935 WALKING THROUGH BEAUTIFUL £ 10,500
oil
Lisa Wright

936 SLEEP NO. 2 £ 8,000
oil on aluminium
Covadonga Valdes

937 IDENTICAL TWINS £ 5,000
48 copperplate etchings on graphite, watercolour and silver
Bella Easton
(edition of 10)

938 CAFE IN COPENHAGEN £ 220
linocut
Rachel Clark
(edition of 40: £150 each)

939 UNDER DOCTOR'S ORDERS £ 500
card, timber veener, plaster, ink
Michael Petch

940 UNTITLED (HEDGE) £ 850
giclée print
Cornelia Baltes
(edition of 5: £680 each)

941 PARISIAN ARCADES – ARCHITECTURAL £ 400
MOMENTS
collage photograph
Maria Bjerg Nørkjær
(edition of 17: £400 each)

942 PARKWAY 1   £ 58,000
oil
Bill Jacklin RA

943 ROSA PROPRINA VISITS THE GARDEN, WINTER £ 14,500
oil
Victoria Crowe

944 UNTITLED (HOUSE)   £ 850
giclée print
Cornelia Baltes
(edition of 5: £680 each)

945 FRAGMENTS OF SOANE   £ 500
card, timber veener, mirror, string, ink and found objects
Michael Petch

946 ANY BUTTER?   £ 1,000
pencil
Percy Savage

947 AN ABHAINN BEAG – THE LITTLE RIVER   £ 1,400
oil
Mary Canty

948 AN ABHAINN MHÓR – THE GREAT RIVER   £ 1,400
oil
Mary Canty

949 PENCIL, PECKHAM   £ 400
digital c-type
Anthony Stokes
(edition of 10: £400 each)

950 TIDE, ST IVES HARBOUR   £ 800
oil
Peter Beeson

951 HOUSE ON THE LOE POOL   £ 750
acrylic
Chris Priestley

952 APPLE TREE IN WINTER £ 8,000
oil
Charlotte Verity

953 CURRENT – HIGH GROUND £ 5,500
oil on linen
Eddie Kennedy

954 THIN RED LINE £ 1,250
oil
Richard Cross

955 RAINBOWS, SWEDEN £ 175
photography
Kensington Leverne
(edition of 30: £125 each)

956 UNTITLED (LANDSCAPE I) £ 450
pencil
Ash Summers

957 TREES £ 1,800
oil
Henry Kondracki

958 DREDGER, PORTISHEAD £ 1,300
oil
Francis Tinsley

959 BONFIRE NIGHT, CLEVELAND SQUARE £ 900
oil
Paul Dilworth

960 FARM ON CARN LLIDI, PEMBROKESHIRE £ 2,950
acrylic and collage
David Humphreys

961 OH SPRING! £ 10,000
oil
Philip Sutton RA

962 DRAGONFLIES ARE ABOUT! £ 36,000
oil
Philip Sutton RA

963 SHADOW £ 5,600
enamelled stainless steel
Bryan Kneale RA

964 POLLINARIA ARTISTS' RESIDENCE, ITALY NFS
resin, wood and steel
Foster Lomas Architects

965 REPRODUCTION PROHIBITED £ 10,000
glazed ceramic
Philip Eglin

966 FIRST WORLD WAR CENTENARY PROJECT, NFS
IMPERIAL WAR MUSEUMS, LONDON. SCALE 1:100
timber plastic
Spencer de Grey RA

967 BOOK: SOLAR TOPOGRAPHY, £ 12,500
THE FARNESE AGRDENS, ROME
brass and paper
Ben Cowd, Thomas Hopkins, Sara Shafiel

968 LIFE LINE £ 11,000
steel, resin and paint
Oliver Barratt

969 LONDON BRIDGE STATION SECTION NFS
wood and metal
Sir Nicholas Grimshaw RA

970 THE SEVEN AGES OF MAN £ 42,000
shaved tennis balls with the artist's hair
Tom Phillips RA

971 DUN LAOGHAIRE HARBOUR MASTERPLAN: NFS
INSTRUMENT OF CHANGE
brass, nickel, silver and cherry wood
Metropolitan Workshop

972 AN INTIMATE CONSTRUCTION £ 2,400
rotring pen, red lead, copy paper
Neal Tanna
(edition of 6: £2,000 each)

973 THE WATCHER'S HOUSE; DINING ROOM PLAN NFS
pencil
Mike Dean

974 DESIGN STUDY NFS
pen and ink wash
Eric Parry RA

975 SHELLEY'S CORRIDOR £ 210
pen and ink
Joanne Edmunds
(edition of 25: £170 each)

976 CROWD: II £ 900
pencil on paper
Stephen Ryan

977 MAGGIE'S PORCH £ 150
giclée print
Nicholas Szczepaniak
(edition of 25: £120 each)

978 PLAZA POOL £ 150
giclée print
Nicholas Szczepaniak
(edition of 25: £120 each)

979 **THE URBAN SHEPHERDESS – CITY PASTORALISM AND A DROVING RENAISSANCE FOR MORE THAN JUST A MEAL** £ 10,000
pencil drawing
Geraldine Ng

980 **DREAM ISLE: LONDON, THE NARRATIVE BLUEPRINT** £ 800
print
Studio 8 Architects
(edition of 10: £800 each)

981 **THE UNFINISHING SCHOOL** £ 350
paper and printed ink
Sam Clark
(edition of 12: £300 each)

982 **THE NEW LONDON NECROPOLIS PLAN I** £ 680
giclée print
Steven Baumann
(edition of 21: £480 each)

983 **THE NEW ARCADIAN PARK** £ 150
paper
Martin Tang
(edition of 50: £100 each)

984 **THE COLLEGE OF FAITH & REASON** £ 2,400
pen and pencil
Dijan Malla

985 **COLUMBARIUM AT COLONIA GÜELL – SECTION** £ 250
giclée print
Eleanor Dodman
(edition of 10: £150 each)

986 **NORFOLK** £ 350
ink
Paul Koralek RA

987 **TREE** £ 350
ink
Paul Koralek RA

988 CONCEPT SKETCH – SHEFFIELD £ 250
ink
Paul Koralek RA

989 SKETCH – SHEFFIELD £ 250
ink
Paul Koralek RA

990 BARN £ 300
ink
Paul Koralek RA

991 BELL £ 300
ink
Paul Koralek RA

992 DHARAVI MASTERPLAN, MUMBAI NFS
(STUDY SKETCHES BY NARINDER SAGOO)
pen and pencil
Lord Foster of Thames Bank RA

993 BLOOMBERG PLACE, LONDON NFS
(STUDY SKETCHES BY NORMAN FOSTER)
pen and pencil
Lord Foster of Thames Bank RA

994 TAIWAN TOWER 3 £ 1,000
digital print
Sir Peter Cook RA
(edition of 6: £1,000 each)

995 TAIWAN TOWER 2 £ 1,000
digital print
Sir Peter Cook RA
(edition of 6: £1,000 each)

996 TAIWAN TOWER I £ 1,000
digital print
Sir Peter Cook RA
(edition of 6: £1,000 each)

997 STAR £ 1,800
oil
Sabrina Rowan Hamilton

998 HEYDAR ALIYEV CENTRE CONSTRUCTION SITE, BAKU, AZERBAIJAN (PHOTOGRAPHS BY HÉLÈNE BINET, 2012) *

digital black and white silver gelatin prints
Zaha Hadid RA
(edition of 6)

999 HEYDAR ALIYEV CENTRE AUDITORIUM, BAKU, AZERBAIJAN (PHOTOGRAPH BY HÉLÈNE BINET, 2012) *

digital black and white silver gelatin print
Zaha Hadid RA
(edition of 6)

1000 HEYDAR ALIYEV CENTRE, SILVER PAINTING £ 50,000

acrylic, vinyl onto gelatinechrome-polyester mounted on D-bond and varnished with UV-resistant polymer
Zaha Hadid RA

1001 NO. 283 £ 12,000

paint on mild steel
Rana Begum

1002 ÉTUDE – B4, 1 £ 1,800

fine art print
Sauerbruch Hutton Architects

1003 PLANS, STUDY FOR MIXED USE DEVELOPMENT NFS

ink and paper
Lord Rogers of Riverside RA

1004 STUDY FOR MIXED USE DEVELOPMENT NFS

computer generated image, ink and paper
Lord Rogers of Riverside RA

1005 LONDON 2012 VELODROME NFS

photograph
Sir Michael Hopkins RA

1006 TURNER CONTEMPORARY: EXTERNAL VIEW (PHOTOGRAPH BY SIMON MENGES) NFS

photographic print
Sir David Chipperfield RA

* Refer to Sales Desk

1007 THE HEPWORTH WAKEFIELD: EXTERNAL VIEW   NFS
     (PHOTOGRAPH BY SIMON MENGES)
photographic print
Sir David Chipperfield RA

1008 STUDY FOR MIXED USE DEVELOPMENT   NFS
computer-generated image, ink and paper
Lord Rogers of Riverside RA

1009 STUDY FOR MIXED USE DEVELOPMENT   NFS
computer-generated image, ink and paper
Lord Rogers of Riverside RA

1010 MONASTERY OF THE HIMALAYAS,   £ 1,300
     CITY OF LONDON: SECTION
giclée print
Na Li
(edition of 6: £900 each)

1011 MONASTERY OF THE HIMALAYAS,   £ 1,300
     CITY OF LONDON: PLAN
giclée print
Na Li
(edition of 6: £900 each)

1012 CORNICE PROPOSAL, PICCADILLY   NFS
polyurethane model board
Richard Deacon RA

1013 MUSEUM FOLKWANG: GALLERY VIEW   NFS
     (PHOTOGRAPH BY UTE ZSCHARNT)
photographic print
Sir David Chipperfield RA

1014 HOUSE OF DIALECTICS (SECTION)   NFS
relief: pencil, coloured pencil
Daniel Schinagl

1015 ROLDAL PILGRIMAGE CENTRE, NORWAY   NFS
hand and computer drawing
Birds Portchmouth Russum Architects

1016 NY VALER CHURCH, NORWAY   NFS
hand and computer drawing
Birds Portchmouth Russum Architects

1017 COMPOSITION 09J £ 4,550
mixed media
Chris Burrows

1018 TYPOLOGY STUDY: TRIESTE £ 140
ink on paper
Chris Raeburn
(edition of 25: £140 each)

1019 DIGITAL PLASTER-SCENARIO III £ 235
(PROJECT TEAM: MANUEL JIMENEZ,
ROBERTO GARCÍA, STELLA DOURTME,
CLAUDIA ERNST, TUTOR:THEODORE SPYROPOULOS)
print
CTRL+M Digitalplaster
(edition of 20: £135 each)

1020 PALESTINIAN MUSEUM, NEAR RAMALLAH NFS
(WITH GROSS MAX)
digital media
Edward Cullinan RA

1021 STUDY CARREL FOR A LONDON CHURCH £ 380
giclée print on hahnemule photorag
Jeffrey James Design
(edition of 25: £230 each)

1022 OYAKO MIZU IRAZU II (FACADE TEST PIECES) NFS
etched brass, plywood frame
Michiko Sumi

1023 PALESTINIAN MUSEUM, NEAR RAMALLAH NFS
(WITH GROSS MAX)
digital media
Edward Cullinan RA

1024 EL MALECON REANIMACION NFS
plaster and nickel silver
Lucy Paton

1025 MUSEUM FOR A PHOTOGRAPHER MEMPHIS, TN   NFS
(DESIGNER: PETER CULLEY, SPATIAL AFFAIRS
BUREAU, MODEL MAKER: ANDREW MONTGOMERY,
RENDERED IMAGE: MATT WAGNER)
balsa wood, inkjet on plywood
Peter Culley, Spatial Affairs Bureau

1026 THE NATURAL SUBLIME: A TRANSPORT   £ 200
INTERFACE ON THE MER DE GLACE, CHAMONIX
digital print
Dave Edwards
(edition of 20: £150 each)

1027 THE SLEEPING RUIN; THE BRICKWORKS   £ 4,000
AT DAWN, 2045
ink and wash
Tom Reynolds

1028 SUBURBANSTUDIO   £ 5,500
paper, inkjet print, wire
Ashton Porter Architects

1029 TURNING DARKNESS INTO LIGHT – THE BOOK   £ 250
OF KELLS, STUDY RETREAT
mixed media
James Flynn & Ashley Clayton
(edition of 20: £95 each)

1030 SKYROOM   £ 350
print on paper
David Kohn Architects
(edition of 5: £280 each)

1031 FIELD OF DREAMS' CONCEPT IMAGE WINNING   NFS
SCHEME FOR 'URBAN SPLASH' (JOCK MCFADYEN
AND CHRIS DYSON)
paint on colour xerox
Christopher Dyson & Jock McFadyen
(edition of 51: £450 each)

1032 PLAYING WITH METAL   NFS
duratrans on lightbox
Eva Jiricna RA

1033 CANADA WATER LIBRARY NFS
film
Piers Gough RA

1034 PLAYING WITH GLASS NFS
duratrans on lightbox
Eva Jiricna RA

1035 AUTONOMOUS INSERTIONS £ 850
digital print
Ellen Ward
(edition of 20: £650 each)

1036 ATHLETES HOUSING, STRATFORD NFS
print on backing
Niall McLaughlin Architects

1037 FRAGMENTS OF A NEW CITY FOR 10 MILLION NFS
PEOPLE, ZULFIKARABAD, PAKISTAN
ink on paper
Keith Williams Architects

1038 L-SHAPED HOUSE (A-MODELS, ARRK) £ 2,000
perspex model with timber base
EM2B Architects

1039 CONVERGENT TERRITORIES II £ 150
print
Aleksandrina Rizova
(edition of 30: £200 each)

1040 MOSQUE OF THE SUN, QUATAR £ 7,500
paper and rapid prototype
Ben Cowd, Thomas Hopkins, Sara Shafiel

1041 THE AUGMENTED INSTRUMENTALIST £ 1,250
backlit framed print on Duratran
Emma-Kate Matthews
(edition of 5: £1,250 eah)

1042 CONVERGENT TERRITORIES I £ 200
print
Aleksandrina Rizova
(edition of 20: £250 each)

1043 NANTYMOEL II £ 1,700
gouache on paper
Jacqueline Poncelet

1044 SURFACE_SPECTRUM £ 950
layered acrylic with coloured film
Surface Architects Ltd

1045 THE HONEY EMPORIUM £ 110
paper and card collage
Bongani Elton Muchemwa

1046 MULTIPLICITY £ 300
print on watercolour paper
Stuart Franks
(edition of 10: £225 each)

1047 EXPLORING THE ARCHITECTURAL INVENTION NFS
OF THE ROYAL ENGINEERS IN THE KENT
COUNTRYSIDE
mixed media collage
Alastair King

1048 REPOSITORY OF THE ETERNAL NOW: SECTION [A-A] NFS
3D print, plywood, digital inkjet print
Robert Ware

1049 CANADA WATER LIBRARY NFS
photograph
Piers Gough RA

1050 CARR JONES HOUSE II (NOW DEMOLISHED) £ 550
photograph
Leonard Manasseh RA

1051 HOUSE IN WEST SUSSEX £ 5,000
photograph and drawings
(Trevor Dannatt RA with John Parry RIBA)

1052 CARR JONES HOUSE I (NOW DEMOLISHED) £ 550
photograph
Leonard Manasseh RA

1053 SOLID II (PHOTOGRAPHS BY PETER COOK) NFS
photograph
Tony Fretton Architects

1054 SOLID II (PHOTOGRAPHS BY PETER COOK)   NFS
photograph
Tony Fretton Architects

1055 BOAT HOUSE, ELY   NFS
inkjet
Michael Manser RA

1056 FAÇADE STUDY, WINDOWLESS HOTEL   NFS
inkjet
Michael Manser RA

1057 GREENFORD HALL, L. B. OF EALING: NFS
PERSPECTIVES OF FORECOURT, DAY AND NIGHT
photograph collage
Sophie Potter @ Dannatt, Johnson Architects
(Trevor Dannatt RA)

1058 WATER TENSION: DIVINE INTERVENTION   £ 1,500
digital print
Christos Markides
(edition of 25: £475 each)

1059 HOLLAND PARK SCHOOL CONCEPT SECTION   £ 1,000
(DRAWING BY MING CHAN)
ink and pencil on film
Aedas Architects Ltd

1060 TIMBER FIN HOUSE (DESIGNED BY NEIL   NFS
DUSHEIKO, MODEL MAKER: MATT HINE)
timber
Neil Dusheiko Architects

1061 BVBV WUPPERTAL RESIDENTIAL DEVELOPMENT £ 2,000
2009–2013
cardboard model, perspex box, base MDF
HE.LO Architects LLP

1062 KERICHO CATHEDRAL, KENYA (JOHN   NFS
McASLAN + PARTNERS, MILLENNIUM MODELS)
card, timber, perspex
John McAslan + Partners

1063 KING'S CROSS STATION NFS
paper, perspex
John McAslan + Partners

1064 CENTRO ARTISTICO CARLOS ACOSTA, CUBA NFS
digital print
Spencer de Grey RA

1065 CENTRO ARTISTICO CARLOS ACOSTA, CUBA. NFS
SCALE 1:250
timber plastic
Spencer de Grey RA

1066 CREATIVE SPACES: CENTRAL SAINT MARTINS £ 4,800
STUDENTS AT THE NEW UNIVERSITY OF THE ARTS
LONDON CAMPUS (PHOTOGRAPHS BY
MAJA DANIELS)
giclée print
Stanton Williams

1067 THE 100 YEAR LEGACY; RECOVERY OF THE £ 4,000
EUSTON ARCH, 2061 (TOM REYNOLDS AND
JAMES CHURCH)
ink and wash
Tom Reynolds

1068 SPACE BETWEEN; WROCLAW OPERA, POLAND £ 300
digital print
Darren Furniss
(edition of 25: £260 each)

1069 COMPONENT ONE SERIES TWO £ 425
walnut and brass
Zoe Fudge

1070 A DAY IN THE LIFE OF A NEW ACTIVITY CENTRE £ 600
FOR THE HOMELESS, PROVIDENCE ROW,
LONDON E1 (PHOTOGRAPH: TIM BROTHERTON)
photographic prints
Featherstone Young
(edition of 10: £420 each)

1071 OLYMPIC LIGHT　　　　　　　　　　　£ 1,500
laser-cut print on paper in light box
Anne Desmet RA
(edition of 3: £1,500 each)

1072 A.I. STATION　　　　　　　　　　　£ 620
photo-etched metal plate
José Manuel Garrido Molina
(edition of 10: £620 each)

1073 SPRING　　　　　　　　　　　£ 300
black ink on paper
Leonard Manasseh RA

1074 NANTYMOEL III　　　　　　　　　　　£ 1,700
gouache on paper
Jacqueline Poncelet

1075 GROWTH　　　　　　　　　　　£ 620
watercolour and coloured ink on watercolour paper
Leonard Manasseh RA

1076 FLY PAST　　　　　　　　　　　£ 620
watercolour and coloured ink on watercolour paper
Leonard Manasseh RA

1077 SOUTH FAÇADE OF VICTORIA LIBRARY　　　　£ 650
(DRAWN & DESIGNED BY PATRICK LYNCH &
LYNCH ARCHITECTS)
watercolour paper, drawing and print
Patrick Lynch Architects

1078 CHURCH OF SAN MAGGIORE, VENICE　　　£ 2,500
pencil and wash
Wesley Richards

1079 THE VICTORIA AND ALBERT MUSEUM; 1873　　　NFS
CAST COURTS (ITALIAN COURT)
(DESIGNED BY GENERAL HENRY SCOTT:
SCHEMATIC RESTORATION BY JULIAN HARRAP
ARCHITECTS (DRAFTSMAN: ANDREW COLES)
photoshop montage
Julian Harrap Architects

1080 'THOSE WERE THE DAYS'. SENATE HOUSE, £ 12,000
CAMBRIDGE, S. ELEVATION. MEASURED
DRAWING, 1939
pencil
Trevor Dannatt RA

1081 A COUPLE OF TREES £ 620
watercolour and coloured ink on watercolour paper
Leonard Manasseh RA

1082 WHARF ROAD £ 250
photograph
Pete Burke
(edition of 20: £150 each)

1083 GORSUCH WORKS DESIGN STUDY, £ 500
EXPLORATION FOR STREET-FACING FAÇADE
digital print
Victoria Collinge
(edition of 10: £350 each)

1084 ARCHI-TÊTES: PRINCE CHARLES £ 295
giclée print
Louis Hellman
(edition of 100: £149 each)

1085 ARCHI-TÊTES: CHRISTOPHER WREN £ 295
giclée print
Louis Hellman
(edition of 100: £149 each)

1086 STUDY FOR MAGGIE'S CENTRE, £ 5,000
ST BARTS, LONDON
watercolour and pencil on paper
Steven Holl

1087 STUDIES FOR MAGGIE'S CENTRE AT ST BARTS £ 5,000
watercolour and charcoal on paper (diptych)
Steven Holl

1088 SYMBIONIC TOWER, ECOLOGICAL £ 3,200
RESEARCH CENTRE, VENIZIAN LAGOON
digital print
Christopher Christophi

1089 BOND UNIVERSITY: GAVIN ROBOTHAM STUDIES £ 10,000
digital print
Sir Peter Cook RA

1090 ISLAND CITY £ 10,000
ink, watercolour and pencil crayon
Sir Peter Cook RA

1091 NEW MARLOWE THEATRE, CANTERBURY NFS
CUTAWAY ISOMETRIC
ink
Keith Williams Architects

1092 [RE]CONSTRUCTED GROUND, NO. 1 £ 1,995
plaster and card
Andrew Morris

1093 THE ETERNAL CITY £ 325
inkjet print
James Redman
(edition of 25: £220 each)

1094 POINT SEVEN (MODEL MAKER: BEN BISEK) £ 3,000
wood, perspex and metal
Dan Brill Architects

1095 DOUBLE COVE, SCALE 1:2000 HONG KONG NFS
timber and acrylic
Lord Rogers of Riverside RA

1096 TSVETNOY CENTRAL MARKET, MOSCOW NFS
(PHOTOGRAPH: CHRIS GASCOIGNE)
digital print
Lifschutz Davidson Sandilands

1097 SANDS PIANIST IV £ 380
digital print
Alexander Hill
(edition of 35: £230 each)

1098 PARK-IN-A-SHED £ 225
digital drawing
Elly Ward
(edition of 25: £225 each)

1099 STUDY OF REPETITION AND VARIATION IN BEDFORD SQUARE £ 25

ink on newsprint
Craig Smith
(edition of 5: £25 each)

1100 SYMBIOTIC AWAKING £ 150

print
Maria Olmos Zunica
(edition of 20: £100 each)

1101 THE DOVER DICHOTOMY I £ 950

relief matte print
Adam Hiles

1102 THE DOVER DICHOTOMY II £ 1,590

matte print
Adam Hiles

1103 SANDS PIANISTS III £ 380

digital print
Alexander Hill
(edition of 35: £230 each)

1104 SOURCE COLLAGE FOR AN INVITED COMPETITION NFS

film prints on perspex
Amin Taha Architects

1105 CITYSCAPE £ 4,500

laser print
Gordon Benson RA
(edition of 6: £2,000 each)

1106 BLACK TRIO (A, B, C) £ 2,900

laser print
Gordon Benson RA
(edition of 6: £1,200 each)

1107 CYPRUS CULTURAL CENTRE NFS

architectural model
Sir Michael Hopkins RA

1108 CONSERVATION IN THE CANOPY – GOLA   NFS
RAINFOREST NATIONAL PARK HEADQUARTERS,
SIERRA LEONE (XENIA GEORGIOU, MICHAEL
RUTHENBURY, ARTICLE 25 DESIGN TEAM,
4D MODELSHOP)
architectural model
Article 25

1109 TWO COTTAGES ON GEORGIAN BAY, CANADA   NFS
wood and card
Dixon Jones Architects

1110 WINDERMERE STEAMBOAT MUSEUM   NFS
wooden model with metal fixings
Carmody Groarke Architects

1111 HOUSE FOR AN EMBALMER AND RADIO HAM,   NFS
CANTERBURY CITY WALL
3D print, wood and steel
William Stanley

1112 DREAM ISLE: LONDON, THE VICTORIAN   NFS
SPONGE CAKE
card, paper and plastic
Studio 8 Architects

1113 LEO YARD HOUSE, CLERKENWELL (YUMA   NFS
YAMA MOTO (AA) STUDENT, CHRIS DYSON
ARCHITECTS)
card and perspex
Christopher Dyson Architects LLP

1114 A HOUSE FOR GEORGE ORWELL (NEGATIVE)   £ 1,000
card
Robert Mainwaring

1115 A HOUSE FOR GEORGE ORWELL (POSITIVE)   £ 1,000
card
Robert Mainwaring

1116 THE WHARVES, DEPTFORD   NFS
(MODEL MAKER: A-MODELS)
plywood and acid-etched brass, stainless steel and nickel silver
Hawkins\Brown

1117 UNIVERSITY ACADEMIC BUILDING (SCALE 1:200)   NFS
(MODELMAKERS: PLP ARCHITECTURE)
wood, bronze and acrylic
Neil Merryweather

1118 HUNEIDI CULTURAL CENTRE: ARCHITECTURAL   NFS
MODEL OF PROJECT FOR KUWAIT (DESIGNERS:
PIERRE BAILLARGEON, RAWIA BAILLARGEON.
MODEL MAKER: SCALES AND MODELS)
wood, brass and acrylic
Mixity Design Ltd

1119 STUDY MODEL FOR HAMPSTED ROAD   NFS
acrylic
Allford Hall Monaghan Morris (AHMM)

1120 VAAL' – NEW CHURCH VÅLER, DETAIL MODEL   NFS
(SCALE 1:100)
birch ply and bronze
Roz Barr Architects

1121 PRIVATE HOUSE, RADLETT   NFS
architectural model
Metropolitan Workshop

1122 FITZROVIA COMPOSITION STUDY   NFS
(DESIGNED BY DSDHA)
metal
DSDHA

1123 GARSINGTON OPERA PAVILLION, WORMSLEY.   NFS
1:100 SECTIONAL MODEL (MODEL BY MILLENNIUM
MODELS)
wood, perspex and plastic
Snell Associates

1124 CATERPILLAR BRIDGE, AMSTERDAM   NFS
(MODEL MAKER: BARTEK RADECKI)
architectural board
Nicholas Hare Architects with Integral Engineering Design

1125 UTILITIES FLOWS WITHIN TAIPEI MAIN STATION   £ 6,500
perspex, rapid prototype, brass and basal wood
Boon Ting Teo

1126 PROPOSED BETHNAL GREEN MEMORIAL £ 12,000
(SCALE 1:32) (ARBOREAL ARCHITECTURE & 3DD)
teak, lime, birch plywood and model board
Arboreal Architecture

1127 BELGRADE CENTRE FOR PROMOTION OF SCIENCE NFS
(LIDA CHARSOULI, NATE KOLBE, TOM ANGIOR)
nylon
SuperFusionLab

1128 TABLE MANORS £ 3,400
sterling silver
Flea Folly Ltd

1129 ELEVATION STUDY 2012 NFS
wood
Eric Parry RA

1130 THE THOUSAND TREES HOUSE (DAVID £ 2,000
LIDDICOAT, SOPHIE GOLDHILL, AIMEE O'CARROLL,
DANIEL GOODACRE, EMILY DOLL, MARIA BAVNHØJ)
plywood, perspex, recycled grey board and lacquer paint
Lidicoat & Goldhill Architects

1131 BEE LIFTS NFS
wood, plastic, felt, paper and perspex
Archmongers and Buchanan Partnership

1132 FERIAS DIVERSORIO NFS
walnut wood, acrylic, bobbins, thread, ceramic, metal and plastic
Hawkins\Brown

1133 THE INTERNATIONAL PRESBYTERIAN CHURCH, £ 7,500
STUDY MODEL NO. 4
walnut
Piercy & Company

1134 FROM LANDSCAPE TO Editions available for sale *
PORTRAIT, SCALE 1:50
stainless steel, walnut and acrylic
Chris Wilkinson RA

* Refer to Sales Desk

1135 VILLAGE V/K 3C: MODEL FOR A DECENT NFS
NEIGHBOURHOOD
plaster and wood
Peter Barber Architects

1136 SLIPSTREAM, RICHARD WILSON – £ 6,000
HEATHROW TERMINAL 2 COMMISSION (SCALE 1:72)
rapid prototype nylon, MDF, *wood and paint*
Richard Wilson RA

1137 BAKU SFERA NFS
wood and acrylic
Anna Liu

1138 DIAL M FOR MONUMENT £ 840
laser-cut handmade cotton rag
Karl Singporewala
(edition of 20: £840 each)

1139 TREEHOUSE IN PARADISE £ 2,000
3D print, nylon and wenge
Elliott Krause & Luis Reis

1140 CANNON PLACE – STRUCTURAL FRAME MODEL NFS
(MODEL MAKER: KANDOR MODELMAKERS)
brass and Swiss pear
Foggo Associates

1141 BASKETBALL ARENA – SECTION, SCALE 1:150 NFS
laser-cut acrylic and vacuum formed PETG
Chris Wilkinson RA

1142 RUGBY STADIUM – SECTION, SCALE 1:150 NFS
laser-cut acrylic and SLS *structure*
Chris Wilkinson RA

1143 ELECTRICITY PYLON COMPETITION NFS
3D white composite powder
Make Architects

1144 LEAF TOWER NFS
acrylic
Squire and Partners

1155 TEMPLE TO PERSPECTIVE, FOR ALAIN DE BOTTON £ 2,600

laser-cut timber veneer
Tom Greenall & Jordan Hodgson
(edition of 3: £2,600 each)

1156 STREET KIOSK NFS

bronze powder cast
Make Architects

1157 IN PRAISE OF TATLIN – ARTIST ARCHITECT ENGINEER (MODEL MAKER: MILLENNIUM MODELS) NFS

wood, glass and photomontage
Dixon Jones Architects

1158 INSECT HOTEL, ST DUNSTAN'S IN THE EAST, LONDON (SCALE 1:5) (DESIGNERS: MICK BRUNDLE, SIMON SWIETOCHOWSKI, CHRISTINA DOUMPIOTI. MODEL MAKERS: DARYL MILES, STEVE ALLEN) NFS

architectural model
Arup Associates

1159 UNIVERSITY OF CYPRUS, FACULTY OF ENGINEERING NFS

architectural model
Sir Michael Hopkins RA

1160 DE-UNION JACK £ 3,200
wood, cable ties and scaffolding net
Jiho Won

1161 FINGER PORTRAIT (SELF) £ 1,850
ham stone
Philip Surey

1162 YOGINI: STUDIES £ 5,000
pencil and crayon on pondicherry
Stephen Cox RA

1163 YOGINI: RAM £ 15,000
pencil and crayon on arches
Stephen Cox RA

1164 CUT BY HAND, YELLOW £ 21,600
postcards on board
David Mach RA

1165 LAYED BACK £ 21,600
playing cards on board
David Mach RA

1166 KRAMPUS £ 500
leather
Rachel Alliston

1167 UNTITLED, 1993–97 (PURCHASED BY THE ROYAL NFS
ACADEMY UNDER THE TERMS OF THE
CHANTREY BEQUEST)
acrylic paint
Phyllida Barlow RA

1168 UNTITLED, 1997 (PURCHASED BY THE ROYAL NFS
ACADEMY UNDER THE TERMS OF THE
CHANTREY BEQUEST)
acrylic paint
Phyllida Barlow RA

1169 UNTITLED, 2004 (PURCHASED BY THE ROYAL NFS
ACADEMY UNDER THE TERMS OF THE
CHANTREY BEQUEST)
acrylic paint
Phyllida Barlow RA

1170 UNTITLED, 1995 (PURCHASED BY THE ROYAL NFS
ACADEMY UNDER THE TERMS OF THE
CHANTREY BEQUEST)
acrylic paint
Phyllida Barlow RA

1171 UNTITLED (PURCHASED BY THE ROYAL NFS
ACADEMY UNDER THE TERMS OF THE
CHANTREY BEQUEST)
acrylic paint
Phyllida Barlow RA

1172 ARAB SPRING (RECLAIMED STEEL) £ 2,200
steel and acrylic
Franceys Allen

1173 CROSSING £ 1,200
wood and acrylic
Morgan Jones

1174 MODEL ASLEEP £ 3,500
charcoal and pastel
James Butler RA

1175 FIGURE *
charcoal
Sir Anthony Caro RA

1176 MODEL RESTING £ 2,760
pencil
Ralph Brown RA

* Refer to Sales Desk

1177 FIGURE *

charcoal

Sir Anthony Caro RA

1178 STANDING MODEL £ 2,760

pencil

Ralph Brown RA

1179 SEATED MODEL £ 2,760

pencil

Ralph Brown RA

1180 MODEL IN CAMISOLE £ 2,760

pencil and wash

Ralph Brown RA

1181 FIGURE *

charcoal

Sir Anthony Caro RA

1182 FIGURE *

charcoal

Sir Anthony Caro RA

1183 TROPICAL PLANT *

ink and charcoal

Sir Anthony Caro RA

1184 LOOP £ 450

colour 3D print

John Bremner

(edition of 8: £450 each)

1185 OBJECT FOR THINKING ABOUT SITTING £ 4,000

MDF, metal, plastic and paint

Frances Richardson

1186 FOUR IDENTICAL SHAPES 82°, 2012 £ 12,000

acrylic with marble powder on plywood

John Carter RA

1187 UNTITLED HOMEWARE NO.13 £ 6,800

flocked objects, steel and glass

Matthew Darbyshire

* Refer to Sales Desk

1188 YOGINI: HORSE £ 60,000

Indian granite
Stephen Cox RA

1189 SPIKE £ 170,000

coat hangers
David Mach RA

1190 ME AS A LION, AS A HERO £ 5,200

steel, mirror and stainless steel
Sahand Hesamiyan
(edition of 3)

1191 THE LOVELY RATS £ 1,850

gold leaf, resin and concrete
Jill Desborough
(edition of 8: £1,850 each)

1192 UNTITLED:TOPPLEDOBJECT £ 25,000

scrim, cement, paint and plywood
Phyllida Barlow RA

1193 SELF-PORTRAIT AS RUBBISH BIN £ 26,000

bronze and paint
Michael Landy RA

1194 COLORED LIFE £ 3,800

hollow dry lacquer
Suguru Takada

1195 KAROSHI £ 3,500

rapid prototyped plaster, veneered MDF *and steel*
Eloise Hawser

1196 TOCCO – PRAIK £ 7,000

polystyrene, oil medium and wood
Ana Genovés

1197 UNTITLED £ 3,700

polyurethane foam and paper lantern
Eloise Hawser

1198 SOME GOD IN THIS PLACE NO. 3 £ 5,500

nickel and zinc-coated steel
Jeff Lowe

1199 GRACE NOTE £ 500
aluminium
Juliet and Jamie Gutch
(edition of 15: £500 each)

1200 SNUG FIT FUNNELS £ 1,200
cement
Jaana Fowler

1201 MATCHES £ 120
porcelain and black stain
Katharine Morling
(edition of 100: £120 each)

1202 TAPE MEASURE £ 100
porcelain and black stain
Katharine Morling
(edition of 100: £100 each)

1203 HATILLO £ 450
porcelain
Loli Cardeñoso

1204 LILY, CURLED UP £ 5,000
bronze
Brian Taylor
(edition of 10: £5,000 each)

1205 GRANDAD AS A PRECOLUMBIAN FUNERARY URN £ 350
ceramic
Geraldine Henegan Barr

1206 PAINT BOX NFS
acrylic paint
Stephen White

**1207 PORTRAIT OF JUSTIN MCLEOD
(THE MAN WITHOUT A FACE)** £ 5,000
chocolate
Eugène Nyee Macki

1208 GOLDEN JAW £ 1,200
rabbit jaw bones, 23ct gold and perspex
Elpida Hadzi-Vasileva
(edition of 10: £1,500 each)

1209 GIRL WITH A RIBBON £ 9,500
bronze
James Butler RA
(edition of 10: £9,500 each)

1210 LIGHT INTERRUPTED £ 1,700
found chair and paint
Caroline Broadhead

1211 CROWN OF THORNS £ 9,500
bronze
Jane Morgan
(edition of 10: £9,500 each)

1212 ALL THAT I HAVE £ 750
egg, sheet music, ceramic, glass and almond wood
Kate Davis and David Moore
(edition of 10: £750 each)

1213 ENTIRETY £ 5,800
steel
Michael Carberry

1214 FOR THE FAMILY £ 4,200
brass
Stephen Lewis

1215 ANNUS MIRABILIS £ 595
ceramic sculpture
Vida Bewley

1216 SPINDLE (L) £ 4,800
steel and polyurethane elastomer
Keith Wilson

1217 CASSIS £ 3,800
bronze
Bryan Kneale RA

1218 CORICELLA £ 4,200
patinated bronze
Bryan Kneale RA

1219 ELECTRA £ 3,600
patinated bronze
Bryan Kneale RA

| 1220 | **CEREBUS** | £ 4,800 |

patinated bronze
Bryan Kneale RA

| 1221 | **NEST** | £ 5,200 |

patinated bronze
Bryan Kneale RA

| 1222 | **BOT** | £ 3,000 |

newspaper, aluminium and sumi ink
Yoshimi Kihara

| 1223 | **WHAT REMAINS OF LA CONTESSA** | £ 950 |

metal wire and textiles
Lynne Brackley

| 1224 | **ORACLE** | £ 10,000 |

bronze
James Butler RA
(edition of 10: £10,000 each)

| 1225 | **TORQUE** | £ 1,500 |

bronze
John Maine RA
(edition of 20: £1,500 each)

| 1226 | **DARK MATTER NOW** | £ 9,900 |

ceramic
Lorne Burrell

| 1227 | **MOSSOM** | £ 1,900 |

fired clay and wire
Alexandra Harley

| 1228 | **SEASCAPE WITH BATHER** | £ 4,500 |

bronze
Ivor Abrahams RA

| 1229 | **POOR TAPED HELICOPTER** | £ 12,500 |

ceramic
Philip Eglin

| 1230 | **SPINDLE (R)** | £ 4,800 |

steel and polyurethane elastomer
Keith Wilson

1231 I CAN ONLY SEE THE CLOUD AND MOUNTAINS £ 1,200
FAR AWAY FROM THERE
plasier
Haruko Yamada

1232 BELL £ 7,200
patinated bronze
Christopher Le Brun PRA
(edition of 6: £7,200 each)

1233 THE GREAT STAN CULLIS NFS
(MODEL FOR PORTRAIT STATUE)
resin
James Butler RA

1234 DRONA £ 1,000
metal
Nimal Jay

1235 HEART AND BRAMBLES £ 4,850
cast aluminium and spray paint
Lana Locke

1236 TWO STICKS £ 2,200
waxed concrete
Eleanor Wright

1237 ORGAN I £ 860
felt, embroidery and toy filling
Ritva Roesler

1238 OIL-PAINTING NFS
glass
Shih-Hsiung Chou

1239 PICCOLA RANA £ 3,000
bronze
Jane Ackroyd
(edition of 25: £3,000 each)

1240 MISS SUGAR CONE UNSURE £ 1,600
ceramic
Anna Barlow

1241 BANANA LOVERS #1 £ 1,680
bronze and travertine
John Alder
(edition of 2: £1,680 each)

1242 BRIDGE OF SIGHS (FOR ELEEZA) £ 48,000
bronze
Michael Sandle RA

1243 HAPPENSTANCE £ 10,000
bronze
Michael Sandle RA

1244 TATTOOED MEMORY £ 26,000
resin, wool, wood, stone and plant
Temsuyanger Longkumer

1245 GROSSULAR £ 2,200
polystyrene, plaster, sand and paint
Ana Genovés

1246 VEDETTA £ 1,500
bronze
Lidia Palumbi
(edition of 12: £1,500 each)

1247 SQUARE AND PARALLELOGRAM: £ 9,850
FOUR UNITS, 2012
aluminium
John Carter RA

1248 WAKE £ 2,250
wood
Tim Long

1249 HENSLOW'S WALK, PANEL NO. 3 £ 6,000
MDF and glass
Susanna Heron
(edition of 6: £6,000 each)

# VIII

1250 BANDED THRONG £ 40,000
Indian granite and goldleaf
Stephen Cox RA

1251 DRAWING 1587 £ 23,580
acrylic and charcoal
Nigel Hall RA

1252 DRONE £ 18,000
alabaster and fibreglass resin
Alison Wilding RA

1253 THREE VASES £ 2,200
clay and wood
Cecile Johnson Soliz

1254 STUDY FOR 'TAUROMACHY' £ 6,600
charcoal
William Tucker RA

1255 GIVE AND TAKE £ 1,850
bowling ball and rubber ball
Stefania Batoeva
(edition of 3: £1,850 each)

1256 SHADOW IN SPACE – 1 £ 480
archival inkjet and mixed media
Ann Christopher RA
(edition of 50: £480 each)

1257 SILENT SPACE £ 16,800
resin and aluminium
Ann Christopher RA
(edition of 5: £16,800 each)

1258 MARE SILICA £ 14,000
glass, vapour shield and polyester resin
Liliane Lijn

1259 LUDLOW RACES £ 810
stoneware and oak
Simon Conolly

1260 DEEP QUARRY £ 5,000
pastel
Kenneth Draper RA

1261 DESERT SPIRIT £ 5,000
pastel
Kenneth Draper RA

1262 UNTITLED 2011 £ 950
cloth and wax
Esther Naor

1263 DRIFTING CLOUDS II £ 3,000
tulip wood, japanese paper, pigments and gesso
Paul Furneaux

1264 PETROL LINE £ 1,150
steel with zinc and colour passivate
Sheila Vollmer

1265 GREY 2012 £ 60,000
plaster and straw
Nicola Hicks

1266 SPILLAGE £ 2,200
silicon and aluminium
Rebecca Griffiths

1267 LAUGHING STOCK £ 1,000
metal
Desmond Cronin

1268 SMOOTH CAT £ 6,400
bronze
Dido Crosby
(edition of 12: £6,400 each)

1269 HUMP WITH A HOLE £ 40,000
charred oak
David Nash RA

1270 SIREN £ 53,125

bronze

William Tucker RA

(edition of 4: £53,125 each)

1271 NOW AND THEN £ 21,600

two silver-plated objects, one flattened by a 250-ton press, suspended on metal wire

Cornelia Parker RA

1272 FEATHER CHILD I £ 12,000

wax, jesmonite, timber and feathers

Lucy Glendinning

(edition of 4: £12,000 each)

1273 WALL MOUNTAIN £ 12,000

painted steel

Almuth Tebbenhoff

1274 FIELDS £ 2,800

ceramic

Ken Eastman

1275 SPIRIT WAVE £ 2,200

steel

Guy Thomas

1276 STUDY FOR RIVER GOD £ 500

flint stone

Robert Grocott

1277 CONSTRUCTION NO. 5 £ 1,600

bronze

Catherine Savigny

1278 BANKSIA, DYNAMIC LAYERS £ 2,650

unglazed porcelain

Nuala O'Donovan

1279 DISCONTINUED £ 3,900

brown paper and moon gold

Harriet Aston

1280 PYGMY RABBIT £ 4,200
bronze
Dido Crosby
(edition of 12: £4,200 each)

1281 FRAGILE ENTOMOLOGY, QUIET £ 1,500
kiln-fused glass powder and wood
Rachel Mary Elliott

1282 THE DROPS OF RAIN MAKE A HOLE IN THE £ 800
STONE, NOT BY VIOLENCE, BUT BY OFTEN FALLING
ceramics
Emma Bagley

1283 SHADOWS OF THE WIND £ 14,500
steel, copper, resin and acrylic
Kenneth Draper RA

1284 ELEPHANT REVENGE I £ 9,800
bronze
Emma Woffenden
(edition of 3: £9,800 each)

1285 ELEPHANT REVENGE II £ 9,800
bronze
Emma Woffenden
(edition of 3: £9,800 each)

1286 BRIDE £ 54,000
bronze
Ralph Brown RA
(edition of 6: £54,000 each)

1287 PRIMAL FECUNDITY £ 1,850
concrete
Victoria Ferrand Scott

1288 SERVICE OBJECT NO. 4 £ 1,950
MDF, paint and rubber strap
Rebecca Griffiths

1289 LONG AND LONG (BEFORE THAT TIME) £ 2,750
bronze
Max Kimber

1290 FLYING BOAT II £ 2,950
aluminium
Geoffrey Clarke RA

1291 EFFECT AND CAUSE £ 4,550
marble and limestone
Ekkehard Altenburger

1292 CUSHLA 2012 £ 12,000
wood, clay, fabric and oil paint
Cathie Pilkington

1293 FLYING BOAT I £ 2,950
aluminium
Geoffrey Clarke RA

1294 FLYING BOAT III £ 2,950
aluminium
Geoffrey Clarke RA

1295 ETON MESS 2012 £ 12,000
wood, clay, leather, fabric, plastic and oil paint
Cathie Pilkington

1296 UNTITLED £ 2,500
ceramic, jesmonite, pigment and wire
Katharine MacCarthy

1297 CLONED MARMOT WITH PETBOTTLE, 2011 £ 3,500
silver-plated bronze
William Sweetlove
(edition of 8: £3,500 each)

1298 ILLUMINATOR 'A' £ 30,000
bronze and laminated MDF
Bill Woodrow RA

1299 ILLUMINATOR 'B' £ 30,000
bronze and laminated MDF
Bill Woodrow RA

1300 BRIGHT STAR £ 12,000
waxed aluminium
Nigel Hall RA

1301 CYLINDERS CELLS £ 1,350
porcelain
Leonora Richardson
(edition of 10: £1,350 each)

1302 HEAD £ 1,117
ceramic
Pauline Hughes

1303 NEVER AN ABSOLUTION £ 1,425
mouth blown glass and enamel
Elinor Andersson

1304 ODALISQUE £ 14,000
bronze
James Butler RA
(edition of 10: £14,000 each)

1305 PREGNANT FAIRY £ 2,500
bronze
Tim Shaw
(edition of 8: £2,500 each)

1306 MONUMENTS OF MELANCHOLY £ 2,000
MDF, porcelain and plywood
Frances Richardson

1307 RATS IN MY KITCHEN £ 4,400
glass
Ruth Dupré

1308 MARRIAGE ROYAL (ROYAL WEDDING) £ 20,000
acrylic resin and polyester
Carles Guilhem

1309 RUINS II £ 2,250
porcelain, oxides, glaze and wire
Mary-Jane Evans

1310 KING £ 7,000
polystyrene, plaster and steel
Javaid Alvi

1311 FLOWER LIFE £ 1,100
steel
Guy Thomas

1312 INVERTED TOILET ROLL £ 650
paper
Panagiotis Dimitropoulos
(edition of 10: £650 each)

1313 DOUBLE SIDED RIVER – THE INTERSECTION £ 4,500
OF THE RIVER THAMES WITH THE
THAMES FLOODPLAIN
cast iron
James Wignall
(edition of 3: £4,000 each)

1314 COCOON II £ 200
wool and plastic bottles
Margaret Barrett

1315 MASTERCHEF £ 2,800
porcelain and steel
Gary Betts

1316 THE TETHER II £ 1,950
oak
John Cobb

1317 TWELVE/STANDING £ 9,400
gouache
Ian McKeever RA

1318 TWELVE/STANDING £ 9,400
gouache
Ian McKeever RA

1319 SAINT £ 50,000
oil
Humphrey Ocean RA

1320 DARK TO LIGHT £ 4,250
acrylic
Mali Morris RA

1321 UNTITLED £ 122,565
mixed media on wood and aluminium
Mimmo Paladino Hon RA

1322 ARMCHAIR PAINTING – UNTITLED £ 10,000
(INNER BEAUTY)
oil
Amikam Toren

1323 THE LAST LAMENT OF THE FIRST BIRD MAN NFS
OF THE UNIVERSE
acrylic, glitter, enamel and rhinestones
Raqib Shaw

1324 MOTHER AND SON £ 24,000
oil
Andrzej Jackowski

1325 JUNK III £ 54,000
oil on linen
Keith Coventry

1326 DUCK CALL £ 6,000
acrylic
Stephen Farthing RA

1327 I KNOW TROUBLE (AND SHE'S MY FRIEND) NFS
oil on linen
Stephen Chambers RA

1328 WHEN TROUBLE MEETS TROUBLE £ 11,500
etching (set of 20)
Stephen Chambers RA
(edition of 25: £9,600 each)

1329 DISTANT ANCESTRY V £ 9,500
oil on linen on board
Ryan Mosley

1330 A LETTER TO JOSHUA NFS
oil
Christopher Le Brun PRA

1331 SOUTHERN SHADE I *
polished MDF
Nigel Hall RA

* Refer to Sales Desk

Lecture Room

1332 MR DARLING'S KISS   £ 7,500
oil on linen
Stephen Chambers RA

1333 WEARABLE PAINTING (BUTTONS)   £ 1,200
oil on fabric, buttons, thread, hanger and nail
Lisa Milroy RA
(edition of 100: £1,200 each)

1334 WEARABLE PAINTING (BARBIES)   £ 7,200
oil, fabric, thread, hanger and nail
Lisa Milroy RA

1335 WEARABLE PAINTING (BLACK FLOWERS)   £ 7,200
oil on silk, fabric, thread, hanger and nail
Lisa Milroy RA

1336 UNTITLED (DOOR HANDLE)   *
acrylic on aluminium
Michael Craig-Martin RA

1337 GURU III   £ 600
charcoal and gouache
Mathew Tom

1338 GRECIAN HEAD, 2012   £ 700
ink on paper
Mark Shields

1339 PRIVATE ROOM   £ 455
c-type print
Miyako Narita
(edition of 20: £320 each)

1340 STAND PROSE, 2011   £ 950
pastel chalk
Rachel Heller

* Refer to Sales Desk

1341 COMPOSITION WITH MARS AND IVORY BLACK £ 1,400
watercolour and gouache
Stuart Dawson

1342 WINTER £ 2,500
acrylic
Alan Rossiter

1343 CUBAN RHYTHMS NFS
oil
Sagen Zac-Varghese

1344 HERERO CADET £ 1,200
photography
Jim Naughten
(edition of 10: £1,000 each)

1345 DEADHAND £ 600
oil
Jane Kelly

1346 ARUNDEL CASTLE £ 500
charcoal
Nancy Thomas

1347 UNTITLED £ 1,250
pencil
Bish White

1348 HAPPY GIRL £ 600
acrylic
Magda Archer

1349 HIP HOP £ 350
aquarelle
Ylva Ziverts

1350 TREES NFS
acrylic and oil
Felix Chadwick-Histed

1351 INTRUSION 1 £ 2,250
mixed media
Henny Acloque

1352 MIRIAM'S ORNITHOLOGY £ 15,000
collage
Eszter Karpati

1353 REHAB £ 750
acrylic
Mulberry Jones

1354 AMBUSH: 16 £ 900
pencil on khadi paper
Sandy Sykes

1355 PARADISE FOUND £ 250
oil
Nigel Barker

1356 011/10 £ 8,000
oil
Andrew Mansfield

1357 PROTEUS XIV £ 19,200
acrylic
Paul Huxley RA

1358 NIGHT DEMONS £ 45,000
oil
John Bellany RA

1359 SERIES 'GHIRLANDA CONTINUA': ITALIA NO. 23 £ 11,000
acrylic
Jennifer Durrant RA

1360 YONDER £ 22,000
acrylic
Frank Bowling RA

1361 THE LONDON STUDIO, 1964–66 £ 24,000
oil on MDF
Anthony Green RA

1362 HANG ON A MINUTE LADS, I'VE GOT A GREAT IDEA… £ 1,800
inkjet, crayon, tippex and graphite
Richard Wilson RA
(edition of 3: £1,700 each)

1363 UNTITLED (TREE NO. 5) £ 78,000
acrylic
Tony Bevan RA

1364 UNTITLED £ 6,250
graphite
David Remfry RA

1365 UNTITLED £ 6,250
graphite and wash
David Remfry RA

1366 SWISHING £ 6,250
watercolour
David Remfry RA

1367 NEWLYN FISH MARKET £ 35,000
oil
Ken Howard RA

1368 TABERNACLE, 2011 £ 36,000
acrylic
Albert Irvin RA

1369 CONSPIRATORS £ 5,000
oil
William Bowyer RA

1370 REMEMBERING CHERNOBYL £ 10,000
encaustic wax and oil
Terry Setch RA

1371 TIREZ £ 96,000
oil and montage
Allen Jones RA

1372 CHILDREN OF THE HOTHOUSE £ 4,250
gouache and tempera
Mick Rooney RA

1373 SOOTHING THE ANIMALS £ 4,250
gouache and tempera
Mick Rooney RA

1374 THE WAVE £ 2,500
oil on panel
Frederick Cuming RA

1375 HEAVEN'S BREATH £ 22,000
mixed media construction
Kenneth Draper RA

1376 HUGH CASSON AND ST PAUL'S, REMEMBERING NFS
HUGH CASSON, 29 NOVEMBER 1999
acrylic
The late Leonard Rosoman RA

1377 THE MEETING, ROYAL ACADEMY OF ARTS, 1979–84 NFS
acrylic
The late Leonard Rosoman RA

1378 THE PROMOTION NO. 1, 1969 NFS
acrylic
The late Leonard Rosoman RA

1379 A BEND IN THE SHRUBBERY NFS
oil
The late Leonard Rosoman RA

1380 BURNT-OUT FIRE APPLIANCE, 1939 NFS
oil
The late Leonard Rosoman RA

1381 PORTRAIT OF LORD ESHER IN A STUDIO AT NFS
THE RCA, 1978
acrylic
The late Leonard Rosoman RA

1382 DIVERGENCE £ 1,500
oil
Alex Gene Morrison

1383 ATTENDANCE £ 1,800
acrylic and pumice
Geoffrey Rigden

1384 AT THE STROKE OF MIDNIGHT £ 8,500
acrylic
Basil Beattie RA

1385 MIDAS MAGIC £ 17,600
oil
Jane Harris

1386 QUAD WRANGLE £ 8,500
acrylic and graphite
Basil Beattie RA

1387 TODAY – LIGHT £ 3,250
acrylic
Mali Morris RA

1388 UNTITLED (8–129) £ 60,000
oil on linen on panel
Thomas Nozkowski

1389 IMP METABOLIC PATHWAY: STEP 1 £ 495
oil
Zachary Beer

1390 BLACKLANDS £ 15,000
acrylic
Gerard Hemsworth

1391 AN ADVANTAGEOUS PROSPECT II £ 800
acrylic on gesso
Catherine Ferguson

1392 INTERNATIONAL ELEGANTO £ 7,850
oil on board
Phillip Allen

1393 TWELVE/STANDING *
oil and acrylic on cotton duck
Ian McKeever RA

1394 COUPLE ORANGE £ 2,800
acrylic
Christian Junghanns

1395 DANCING AROUND MIDNIGHT £ 35,000
acrylic
Maurice Cockrill RA

* Refer to Sales Desk

1396 PROTEST, LAMBETH TOWN HALL £ 9,000
oil
Anthony Eyton RA

1397 TAPESTRY £ 12,000
oil
Anthony Eyton RA

1398 REDWOODS £ 14,400
acrylic and mixed media
Mick Moon RA

1399 KISS 23 £ 1,500
acrylic
David Oates

1400 AEGEAN NOTEBOOK £ 16,000
oil
Sonia Lawson RA

1401 POSTCARD FROM PROVENCE I £ 16,000
oil
Sonia Lawson RA

1402 SERIES 'GHIRLANDA CONTINUA': ITALIA NO. 24 £ 9,600
acrylic
Jennifer Durrant RA

1403 SURFACE £ 18,000
oil
Humphrey Ocean RA

1404 INCARNADINE £ 20,000
oil on canvas on board
Jeffery Camp RA

1405 FLOWER BED £ 3,500
acrylic, mixed media, flock fibre on board
Ivor Abrahams RA

1406 SELINE £ 2,750
cut-out paper and watercolour
Ivor Abrahams RA

1407 MISS MYTH £ 12,000
egg tempera
David Tindle RA

1408 JOURNEY TO THE CENTRE OF THE EARTH £ 12,500
watercolour and pencil
Chris Orr RA

1409 A FAIRY TALE IN A FOREST £ 36,000
oil
Philip Sutton RA

1410 LUNACY £ 9,450
oil
Timothy Hyman RA

1411 FINESTRA VENEZIANA VENESSIA 3 £ 35,000
acrylic, glass, lattino glass relief and resin relief on
wood relief
Joe Tilson RA

1412 HYDRANGEA – FADING FROM BLUE £ 8,000
oil
Olwyn Bowey RA

1413 A GROUP OF PLANTS £ 8,000
oil
Olwyn Bowey RA

1414 DORA AT ORIEL £ 50,000
oil
Ken Howard RA

1415 BURNT AUTUMN STUBBLE – REGROWTH £ 14,000
acrylic
Anthony Whishaw RA

1416 CANTO 114 £ 30,000
acrylic and glass on canvas on wood
Joe Tilson RA

1417 SASH £ 33,600
oil
Christopher Le Brun PRA

1418 SELF-PORTRAIT HEAD £ 12,500
charcoal
Tony Bevan RA

1419 FISH STALL, BRIXTON MARKET £ 21,000
oil
Anthony Eyton RA

1420 SKIATHOS £ 15,000
acrylic
Gus Cummins RA

1421 BUTTERFLY £ 12,000
mixed media
Fathi Hassan

1422 SERIES 'GHIRLANDA CONTINUA': ITALIA NO. 2 £ 5,000
acrylic on canvas on wood
Jennifer Durrant RA

1423 REFLEX £ 16,000
dark green granite
John Maine RA

1424 MITRE £ 16,500
Swedish granite
John Maine RA

1425 FULL CIRCLE £ 12,000
Indian granite
John Maine RA

1426 OUTER RING £ 12,000
Indian granite
John Maine RA

1427 VORTEX £ 12,500
Norweigan granite
John Maine RA

1428 RELIQUARY HOUSE *
steel and concrete
Sir Anthony Caro RA

* Refer to Sales Desk

1429 AT THE CIRCUS £ 7,850
perspex, aluminium, foam and pvc
Phillip King RA

1430 RING REEL MAQUETTE £ 7,850
steel, foam and PVC
Phillip King RA

1431 FIELD – DAY £ 7,850
steel, foam PVC and aluminium
Phillip King RA

1432 CADEROUSEL £ 6,850
perspex, foam PVC and aluminium
Phillip King RA

1433 HEART SPIRAL £ 5,850
steel and foam PVC
Phillip King RA

1434 RECLINE £ 10,500
stainless steel and deep crimson epoxy paint
Dhruva Mistry RA

1435 SEATED £ 10,500
stainless steel and cobalt deep epoxy paint
Dhruva Mistry RA

1436 FRAU MANETS RECHTER FUß *
oil
Georg Baselitz Hon RA

1437 WORK NO. 623, DOGS £ 66,000
flashing green neon
Martin Creed
(edition of 3: £66,000 each)

1438 STEVIE £ 45,000
oil
Dexter Dalwood

1439 UNTITLED (SMALL COLLAGE NO. 26) £ 4,500
mixed media on archive paper on board
Fiona Rae RA

1440 THE FIELD £ 230,000
gloss on aluminium
Gary Hume RA

1441 DOLORES £ 3,000
ink, thread and beads
Denise de Cordova

1442 ELECTRA £ 17,000
oil
Stephen Farthing RA

1443 PAINTING FOR D.A, V.A £ 5,400
oil on panel
Estelle Thompson

1444 CONSUMED £ 18,000
oil
Emma Biggs and Matthew Collings

* Refer to Sales Desk

1445 DESK CHAIR £ 100,000
acrylic on aluminium
Michael Craig-Martin RA

1446 UPSET £ 165,000
acrylic
Tracey Emin RA

1447 MIGRAINE WEATHER £ 3,300
oil on linen
James Fisher

1448 WEDDED TO SILENCE £ 3,300
oil on linen
James Fisher

1449 BATTERY PARK UNDER THE TREE, NYC 1 £ 58,000
oil
Bill Jacklin RA

1450 DIDO IN CARTHAGE £ 96,000
oil
Christopher Le Brun PRA

1451 THE ANATOMICAL MAN £ 1,200
(SELF PORTRAIT WITH TATTOOS)
c-type print
Richard Sawdon Smith
(edition of 11: £1,200 each)

1452 UNTITLED £ 350
mixed
Philippa Johnson

1453 DEADLY MOUNTAIN 6, FROM THE SERIES £ 650
DEADLY MOUNTAINS
photograph
Jochen Klein
(edition of 5: £500 each)

1454 THE CLARENCE NO. 1 £ 495
photograph
Alexandra Simms
(edition of 10: £400 each)

1455 CROSSWIND £ 3,600

mixed media
Lyndon Douglas
(edition of 10: £3,300 each)

1456 PHOENIX PLACE WC1 £ 375

silver gelatin print
Robert Moye & Peter Young
(edition of 20: £275 each)

1457 THE MILKMAID £ 1,400

photograph
Raeda Saadeh
(edition of 10*)

1458 VANITAS, CLEANING £ 950

archival pigment print
Peter Abrahams
(edition of 5: £800 each)

1459 YELLOW £ 850

lithograph
Guler Ates
(edition of 15: £550 each)

1460 CITY BREAK £ 350

photograph
Nigel Lord
(edition of 50: £200 each)

1461 NDUTU £ 6,500

ultrachrome in acrylic block
David Usill
(edition of 12: £6,500 each)

1462 EXISTING IN COSTUME 8 £ 1,500

c-print
Chan-Hyo Bae
(edition of 15: £1,200 each)

1463 GREETING CARDS £ 700

inkjet print
Julie Born Schwartz
(edition of 3: £500 each)

* Refer to Sales Desk

1464 CHESS KING, BRICK LANE (E1) £ 550
photograph
Hathaichanok Julareesuk
(edition of 2: £280 each)

1465 A POINT OF DISCORD: HER APPLES £ 600
gelatin silver print
Jieun Kim
(edition of 25: £520 each)

1466 MALCOLM IN FLYHOUSE £ 1,100
photograph
Christopher Moon
(edition of 50: £950 each)

1467 PUDONG I, SHANGHAI *
chromogenic colour print
Nadav Kander

1468 THE CORRIDOR £ 2,700
c-type print
Liane Lang
(edition of 6: £2,200 each)

1469 HERERO LADY £ 1,200
photograph
Jim Naughten
(edition of 10: £1,000 each)

1470 SPOTLIGHT (2) £ 12,000
egg tempera
David Tindle RA

1471 THE PHOTO £ 700
giclée print
Quentin Blake
(edition of 100: £400 each)

1472 COMRADES IN ART £ 700
giclée print
Quentin Blake
(edition of 100: £400 each)

* Refer to Sales Desk

1473 ON THE BEACH £ 700
giclée print
Quentin Blake
(edition of 100: £400 each)

1474 RECLINING NUDE NFS
bronze
Kiki Smith
(edition of 3)

List of
Exhibitors

Abbaro, Besheer, Flat B, 4 Osborne Road, London N13 5PS, **749**

ABRAHAMS, Prof. Ivor, RA, 33 Artillery Road, Ramsgate, Kent CT11 8PT, **548, 608, 888, 1228, 1405, 1406**

Abrahams, Peter, 151A Moselle Avenue, London N22 6EU, **1458**

Abrams, Martin, Flat 14, Yew House, Shardeloes Road, London SE14 6RX, **469**

Abts, Tomma, Greengrassi, London **817**

Ackling, Roger, Courtesy of the Artist and Annely Juda Fine Art, 23 Dering Street, London W1S 1AW, **309, 310**

Ackroyd, Jane, 34 Winton Avenue, London N11 2AT, **1239**

ACKROYD, Prof. Norman, CBE RA, 1 Morocco Street, London SE1 3HB, **558, 559, 560, 561, 562, 563**

Acloque, Henny, 5 Shottendane Road, London SW6 5TJ, **94, 1351**

Adams, Alexander, c/o 20 Spring Gardens Place, Cardiff CF24 1QZ, **204, 311**

Aedas Architects Ltd, c/o Peter Runacres, 5-8 Hardwick Street, London EC1R 4RG, **1059**

Afnan, Maliheh, c/o Rose Issa Projects, 269 Kensington High Street, London W8 6NA, **504**

Ajerman, Michael, 108A Clapham Manor Street, London SW4 6EA, **120, 496**

Alamir, Alaleh, c/o Rose Issa Projects, 269 Kensington High Street, London W8 6NA, **606**

Alder, John, Pennistones, Town Mill, Wiveliscombe, Somerset TA4 2LY, **1241**

Alexander, Naomi, 6 The Bishops Avenue, London N2 0AN, **171**

Allen, Franceys, Willow Farm, Pettaugh Road, Stonham Aspal, Stowmarket, Suffolk IP14 6AX, **1172**

Allen, Phillip, 3 Highgate Walk, London SE23 3YA, **413, 1392**

Allen, Tim, 9 Steeple Court, Coventry Road, London E1 5QZ, **406**

Ashton Porter Architects, c/o Abigail Ashton, 11 Second Avenue, Bush Hill Park, Enfield EN1 1BT, **1028**

Aston, Harriet, 28 Ravenswood Road, Bristol BS6 6BW, **1279**

Ates, Guler, Flat 6, 63 Westcombe Park Road, London SE3 7QT, **743, 1459**

Austen, David, c/o Anthony Reynolds Gallery, 60 Great Marlborough Street, London W1F 7BG, **366**

Austin, Marcus, 84 North Street, Isleworth TW7 6RE, **205**

AYRES, Gillian, CBE RA, Courtesy of Alan Cristea Gallery, 31 & 34 Cork Street, London W1S 3NU, **527, 528, 531, 533, 596, 616**

B

Baalbaki, Ayman, c/o Rose Issa Projects, 269 Kensington High Street, London W8 6NA, **257**

Baalbaki, Mohamed-Said, c/o Rose Issa Projects, 269 Kensington High Street, London W8 6NA, **503**

Bae, Chan-Hyo, 12 Abbey Court, Abbey Road, London NW8 0AU, **1462**

Bagley, Emma, 55 Dunholme Road, Edmonton, London N9 9QS, **1282**

Bailey, Liz, 10 Grove Terrace, Highgate Road, London NW5 1PH, **217**

Baker, Richard, 26 Aviary Place, Leeds LS12 2NP, **235, 447**

Baldwin, Dan, c/o CCA Galleries, Greenhills Estate, Tilford Road, Tilford, Surrey GU10 2DZ, **660**

Ball, Rob, 8 Railway Avenue, Whitstable, Kent CT5 1LJ, **706**

Ballard, Morag, Boskennal Farmhouse, St Buryan, Penzance, Cornwall TR19 6DF, **368**

Baltes, Cornelia, c/o Kunstwerk Koln e.V., Deutz-Mulheimerstr 127-129, Cologne, 51063, Germany, **940, 944**

Banthorpe, Trevor, 59 Abbotsford Avenue, London N15 3BT, **540, 732**

Barker, Nigel, 50 Park Street, Baldock, Herts SG7 6DY, **1355**

Barlow, Anna, Flat A, 74 Highbury New Park, London N5 2DJ, **1240**

BARLOW, Phyllida, RA Elect, c/o Royal Academy of
Arts, **1167, 1168, 1169, 1170, 1171**, c/o Hauser and Wirth,
London, **1192**

Barnes, Jeanette, 12 Crestbrook Place, Green Lanes,
London N13 5SB, **759**

The Baron, 2 Newhouse Farm Cottages , Wick Street,
Firle, Lewes, East Sussex BN8 6ND, **59**

Barr, Roz, 111-113 St John Street, London EC1V 4JA, **1120**

Barratt, Oliver, 5 Manor Farm Cottage, Ightham,
Sevenoaks, Kent TN15 9DG, **968**

Barrett, Margaret, 71 Dornden Drive, Langton Green,
Tunbridge Wells, Kent TN3 0AG, **1314**

Bartlett, Adrian, 132 Kennington Park Road, London
SE11 4DJ, **735**

BASELITZ, Georg, Hon RA, Courtesy of Artist's Studio,
1436

Batakov, Nikolai, Kolesnikova str. 11, Kaliningrad, 236010,
Russia, **763**

Batchelor, David, Courtesy of the Artist, **7, 279**

Batoeva, Stefania, 80A Naylor Road, London SE15 1QQ,
1255

Baumann, Steven, 144 Camden Road, London NW1 9HP,
982

Baumgartner, Christiane, Courtesy of Alan Cristea
Gallery, 31 & 34 Cork Street, London W1S 3NU, **578**

Bawden, Richard, 72 Benton Street, Hadleigh, Suffolk
IP7 5AT, **620**

Baxter, Glen, c/o Flowers Gallery, 82 Kingsland Road,
London E2 8DP, **634**

Beadle, Joan, 23 Grange Road, Chorlton, Manchester
M21 9NZ, **795**

BEATTIE, Basil, RA, James Hyman Gallery,
5 Saville Row, London W1S 3PD, **477, 478, 486, 487, 1384,
1386**

Becker, Paul, 2E King Street, Newcastle Upon Tyne
NE1 3UQ, **113, 273**

Beer, Zachary, 44 Newton Road, Cambridge CB2 8AL, **1389**

Beeson, Peter, 12 Bellair Terrace, St Ives, Cornwall TR26 1JR, **950**

Begum, Rana, Courtesy of Bischoff/Weiss, 14A Hay House, London W1J 8NZ, **403, 1001**

BELLANY, Dr John, CBE RA, Beaux Arts London, 22 Cork Street, London W1S 3NA, **48, 849, 1358**

Bennett, Fiona Marianne, 30 Twyford Gardens, Bishops Stortford, Herts CM23 3EH, **668**

Bennett, Michael, Bromstone, Welshmill Road, Frome, Somerset BA11 2LA, **390**

Bennett, Terence, Rambler Cottage, 43 Main Street, Sprotbrough, Doncaster DN5 7RH, **103**

Bennetts Associates Architects, c/o Elizabeth Walker, 1 Rawstorne Place, London EC1V 7NL, **1146**

BENSON, Prof. Gordon, OBE RA, Benson & Forsyth LLP, 37D Mildmay Grove North, London N1 4RH, **879, 1105, 1106**

Ben-Zenou, Helena, 22 Oakfield Court, Haslemere Road, London N8 9RA, **927**

BERG, The late Adrian, RA, c/o Royal Academy of Arts, **42, 44, 45, 46**

Betts, Gary, 11 Magnolia Wharf, Strand on the Green, London W4 3NY, **1315**

BEVAN, Tony, RA, 20 Blackheath Park, London SE3 9RP, **587, 592**, Ben Brown Fine Arts, 21 Cork Street, London W1S 3LZ, **1363, 1418**

Bewley, Vida, Ashbrook Farm, 222 Melton Road, Six Hills, Melton Mowbray LE14 3PU, **1215**

Bick, Andrew, 116 Manor Lane, London SE12 8LR, **262, 473**

Biggs and Collings, Emma and Matthew, Church House, 2 Church Lane, Northwold, Norfolk IP26 5LY, **1444**

Bill, Peter, 12A Gloucester Road, London SW7 4RB, **261**

Birds Portchmouth Russum Architects, c/o Mike Russum, Unit 11, Union Wharf, 23 Wenlock Road, London N1 7SB, **1015, 1016**

BLACKADDER, Dame Elizabeth, DBE RA, 57 Fountainhall Road, Edinburgh EH9 2LH, **24, 321, 845**, Glasgow Print Studio, 103 Trongate, Glasgow G1 5HD, **780, 781, 782**

BLAKE, Prof. Quentin, CBE RDI Hon Fellow RA, Flat 8, 30 Bramham Gardens, London SW5 0HF, **1471, 1472, 1473**

Boele-Keimer, Vera, 48 Kingsdown Parade, Bristol BS6 5UF, **614**

Born Schwartz, Julie, 71 Manor Avenue, London SE4 1TD, **1463**

Borrington, David, 7 Lewis Lane, Arlesey, Bedfordshire SG15 6FB, **757**

Boshier, Derek, c/o Flowers Gallery, 82 Kingsland Road, London E2 8DP, **4, 154**

Bowers, Karen, Boxtree Cottage, Pancake Hill, Lower Chedworth, Gloucestershire GL54 4AW, **160**

BOWEY, Olwyn, RA, Random Cottage, Peace Lane, Heyshott, Midhurst, West Sussex GU29 0DF, **451, 484, 883, 1412, 1413**

BOWLING, Frank, OBE RA, Hales Gallery, Tea Building, 7 Bethnal Green Road, London E1 6LA, **2, 20, 382, 383, 384, 1360**

Bowyer, Francis, 12 Gainsborough Road, London W4 1NJ, **202**

BOWYER, William, RA, 12 Cleveland Avenue, London W4 1SN, **32, 33, 54, 440, 446, 1369**

Boyd & Evans, c/o Flowers Gallery, 82 Kingsland Road, London E2 8DP, **508**

Boyd, Gabriella, 282 Kingsland Road, London E8 4DG, **111, 347**

Boyd, Graham, Blackapple, 54 Scatterdells Lane, Chipperfield, Hertfordshire WD4 9EX, **303**

Brackley, Lynne, 94A, Uplands Road, London N8 9NJ, **1223**

Bremner, John, 103 Lightfoot Road, London N8 7JL, **1184**

Bridges, Benjamin, 42 Thackeray Court, Blythe Road, London W14 0PW, **437**

Bridgland, Adam, Flat D, 81 Queens Drive, London N4 2BE, **658**

Bridgland, Sarah, 4 Stewards Close, Sutton, Ely, Cambridgeshire CB6 2NQ, **173, 174**

Brill, Dan, 37 Southgate Street, Winchester, Hampshire, SO23 9EH, **1094**

Broadhead, Caroline, c/o Marsden Woo Gallery, 17-18 Great Sutton Street, London EC1V 0DN, **1210**

Brodholt, Gail, Half Moon Studio, B23 Parkhall Industrial Estate, 40 Martell Road, London SE21 8EN, **761, 762**

Broom, Orlanda, 12 Geraldine Road, London W4 3PA, **270**

BROWN, Ralph, RA, Southanger Farm, Cowcombe Hill, Chalford, Stroud, Gloucestershire GL6 8HP, **1176, 1178, 1179, 1180, 1286**

Browne, Alice, 1 Chestnut House, 37 Sycamore Avenue, London E3 5RZ, **288, 463**

Burke, Pete, 15B Queensdown Road, London E5 8NN, **1082**

Burns, Patricia, 6 Seminary Villas, Blackpool, Cork, Ireland, **890**

Burnstone, Deborah, 25 Lucerne Road, London N5 1TZ, **415, 467**

Burrell, Lorne, 57 Dudley Court, 36 Endell Street, London WC2H 9RQ, **1226**

Burrows, Chris, 21A High Street, Rochester, Kent ME1 1LN, **1017**

Burton, Simon, 51 Talfourd Road, London SE15 5NN, **143**

Bustin, Jane, 1 Hillside Gardens, London N6 5SU, **828, 829**

BUTLER, James, MBE RA, Valley Farm Studios, Radway, Warwick, CV35 0UJ, **1174, 1209, 1224, 1233, 1304**

Butterworth, John, 10 Railway Avenue, Whitstable, Kent CT5 1LJ, **392**

Byrne, John, c/o Open Eye Gallery, 34 Abercromby Place, Edinburgh EH3 6QE, **843, 876**

C

Callaghan, Francis, 10 St Thomas Park, Lymington, Hampshire, SO41 9NF, **16, 441**

CAMP, Jeffery, RA, Art Space Gallery, 84 St Peter's Street, London N1 8JS, **92, 95, 196, 328, 455, 1404**

Campbell, Kelly, 8 Fielding Close, Llanrumney, Cardiff, Glamorgan, CF3 5NE, **337**

Canti, Oliver, Coxhill Cottage, Churchstanton, Taunton, Somerset, TA3 7RL, **916**

Canty, Mary, Block A, No. 5, Iveagh Buildings,
New Bride Street, Dublin 8, Ireland, **947, 948**

Carberry, Michael, 1 Sunnybank, Ford Village, Aylesbury,
Buckinghamshire HP17 8XH, **1213**

Cardeñoso, Loli, 26 Alma Square, London NW8 9PY, **1203**

Carmody Groarke Architects, c/o Alex Stevens,
21 Denmark Street, London WC2H 8NA, **1110**

CARO, Sir Anthony, OM CBE RA, c/o Royal Academy of
Arts, **1175, 1177, 1181, 1182, 1183, 1428**

Carpanini, David L, Fernlea, 145 Rugby Road, Milverton,
Leamington Spa, Warwickshire CV32 6DJ, **707**

Carraro, Paolo, 72 Hazlewood Tower, Golborne Gardens,
London W10 5DU, **799**

Carrick, Nick, 69 Grange Road, Hove, Sussex BN3 5HW,
289

CARTER, John, RA, The Redfern Gallery, 20 Cork Street,
London W1S 3HL, **679, 688, 691, 1186, 1247**

Carter, Tony, 2 Little Brownings, London SE23 3XJ, **128**

Cartwright, Richard, c/o The Adam Gallery, 24 Cork
Street, London W1S 3NJ, **97, 906**

Casey, Comhghall, 127 Nephin Road, Cabra, Dublin 7,
Ireland, **417**

Cave, Sue, Timberyard Cottage, Enstone Road, Little
Tew, Chipping Norton, Oxfordshire OX7 4HZ, **696**

Chadwick-Histed, Felix, 3 Davenport Close, Teddington
TW11 9EF, **1350**

Chambers, Derek, 8 South Entrance, Saxmundham,
Suffolk IP17 1DQ, **657**

CHAMBERS, Stephen, RA, 31 Sotheby Road, London
N5 2UP, **579, 580, 581, 1327, 1328, 1332**

Chapman, Chris, Flat 3, 10 Queens Park Avenue,
Bournemouth, BH8 9LG, **304**

Charman, George, Flat 8, Acme Fire Station, 30 Gillender
Street, London E14 6RH, **670**

CHIPPERFIELD, Prof. Sir David, CBE RA, David
Chipperfield Architects, 11 York Road, London SE1 7NX,
1006, 1007, 1013

Chou, Shih-Hsiung, Flat 1, 308 St Paul's Road, London N1 2LF, **1238**

Christian, Perienne, 7A Brockley Grove, London SE4 1QX, **169, 170**

CHRISTOPHER, Ann, RA, c/o Royal Academy of Arts, **516, 517, 518, 1256, 1257**

Christophi, Christopher, 13 Lordsbury Field, Wallington, Surrey
SM6 9PE, **1088**

Ciechanowska, Joanna, 2 Clydesdale Gardens, Richmond, Surrey TW10 5EF, **507**

Clark, Rachel, 24 Cranedown, Lewes, East Sussex BN7 3NA, **938**

Clark, Sam, 2 Town Quay, Blacksmiths Lane, Laleham, Staines, TW18 1UA, **981**

Clarke, Benjamin, 2 Crumps Butts, Bicester OX26 6EB, **370**

CLARKE, Carey, Hon Member Ex Officio PPRHA, 16 Joyce Avenue, Foxrock, Dublin 18, Ireland, **885**

CLARKE, Geoffrey, RA, Burnt House Farm, Hartest, Bury St Edmunds, Suffolk IP29 4EQ, **1290, 1293, 1294**

Clarke, Graham, White Cottage, Green Lane, Boughton Monchelsea, Maidstone, Kent ME17 4LF, **731**

Clarke, Sheena, 38A Dancer Road, Richmond, Surrey TW9 4LA, **494**

Clarke, Thomas, Dorset View, Hale Road, Hale, Hampshire SP6 2NW, **313**

Clegg, Oliver, The Old Cottage, Church Street, Crondall, Farnham, Surrey GU10 5QQ, **131**

Clerihew, David, 35 Melford Road, London SE22 0AG, **682**

Cobb, John, 3 Hackney Terrace, Melton, Woodbridge, Suffolk IP12 1NN, **1316**

COCKRILL, Prof. Maurice, RA, c/o Royal Academy of Arts, **5, 162, 163, 464, 465, 1395**

Coe, Michael, 26 Paston Ridings, Paston, Peterborough PE4 7YG, **324**

Coen, Francis, 19 Boxberry Gardens, Walnut Tree, Milton Keynes, Buckinghamshire MK7 7EN, **126, 127**

Cohen, Yosef, 38 Commonfields, West End, Woking, Surrey GU24 9HZ, **425**

Cohn, Suki, 5A Uplands Road, London N8 9NN, **514**

Colclough, Gary, 31 Ollerton Green, London E3 2LB, **329**

Coldwell, Paul, 86 Oakfield Rd, London N4 4LB, **568**

Cole, Austin, 135 Linkfield Road, Isleworth TW7 6QW, **526**

Coleman, Amanda, Pond Cottage, 29 Toddington Road, Tebworth, Leighton Buzzard, Bedfordshire LU7 9QD, **105**

Coleman, Rebecca, 24C Streatley Road, London NW6 7LS, **709**

Collinge, Victoria, 47 Dulwich Road, First floor flat, London SE24 0NJ, **1083**

Collini, Liz, 29 Methuen Park, London N10 2JR, **753**

Conolly, Simon, Lower Earnstrey Park Farm, Tugford, Craven Arms, Shropshire, SY7 9HT, **1259**

COOK, Prof. Sir Peter, RA, CRAB Studio Architects, 50A Rosebery Avenue, London EC1R 4RP, **994, 995, 996, 1089, 1090**

Coombs, Michael, 10 Bailey Mews, London SW2 1LR, **420**

COOPER, Eileen, RA, Art First Gallery, 21 Eastcastle Street, London W1W 8DD, **31, 132, 649, 651, 652, 653**

Cooper, Emily Jane, 153 Camberwell Road, London SE5 0HB, **427**

Corbin-Bishop, Matthew, c/o Rose Issa Projects, 269 Kensington High Street, London W8 6NA, **93, 192**

Cory, Charlotte, 10 Park Vista, London SE10 9LZ, **665**

Costa, Rodrigo, R. S. Salvador, 164, 1º Dtº, Oliveira do Douro, Vila Nova de Gaia, 4430-227, Portugal, **373**

Courtney, Anne, 5 Coxhill Crescent, River, Dover, Kent CT17 0PZ, **70**

Cousins, Tim, 1 Chestnut Rise, London SE18 1RJ, **355**

Coventry, Keith, Courtesy of the Artist and Pace Gallery Ltd, Liberty House, 222 Regents Street, London W1B 5TR, **1325**

Cowd, Ben, Sarah Shafili, Thomas Hopkins, 6 Bishops House, 37 The Green, Great Bowden, Market Harborough, Leicestershire LE16 7EU, **967, 1040**

COX, Stephen, RA, Lower House Farm, Coreley, Nr
   Ludlow, Shropshire, SY8 3AS, **1162, 1163, 1188, 1250**
CRAIG-MARTIN, Michael, CBE RA, Courtesy of Alan
   Cristea Gallery, 31 & 34 Cork Street, London WIS 3NU,
   564, 565, 566, 567, Courtesy Gagosian Gallery, **1336,
   1445**
Cranston, Andrew, Flat 1-2, 14 Great George Street,
   Glasgow GI2 8NA, **448**
Creed, Martin, Courtesy of Hauser & Wirth, London,
   297, 1437
Cronin, Desmond, Upper Flat, 127 Coleman Road,
   London SE5 7TF, **1267**
Crosby, Dido, 52 Thorne Road, London SW8 2BY, **1268,
   1280**
Cross, Richard, 10 Fort Street, Clitheroe BB7 IBY, **954**
Crossley, John, 30 Clarendon Rise, London SE13 5EY, **492**
Crowe, Victoria, Bank House, Main Street, West Linton,
   Peeblesshire EH46 7EE, **943**
Crowley, Graham, 42 Dunstans Road, London SE22 OHQ,
   921
CTRL+M, Flat 10, Elissa Court, 3 Chitty Street, London
   WIT 4AT, **1019**
CULLINAN, Edward, CBE RA, Edward Cullinan
   Architects, 1 Baldwin Terrace, London NI 7RU, **535,
   1020, 1023**
CUMING, Frederick, RA Hon DLitt, The Gables,
   Wittersham Road, Iden, East Sussex TN31 7UY, **9, 489,
   553, 554, 910, 1374**
CUMMINS, Gus, RA, Harpsichord House, Cobourg
   Place, Hastings, Sussex TN34 3HY, **249, 293, 929,
   1420**
Cutler, Sally, 25A Gairloch Road, London SE5 8NG, **770**

D   Dalby, Simon, 4-17-31-702 Nishi-Azabu, Minato-Ku,
   Tokyo, 106-0031, Japan, **330**
   Daltry, Hilary, 20 Mildmay Grove South, London NI 4RL,
   646

Dalwood, Dexter, Courtesy Gagosian Gallery, 6-24 Britannia Street, London WC1X 9JD, **1438**

Dannatt, Joan, 8 St Mary's Grove, London N1 2NT, **515**

DANNATT, Prof. Trevor, RA, Dannat, Johnson Architects, 52c Borough High Street, London SE1 0HS, **1051, 1057, 1080**

Dant, Adam, 15 Club Row, London E2 7EY, **633, 764**

Darbyshire, Matthew, 2 Herald Street, London E2 6JT, **1187**

Davenport, Ian, Courtesy of Waddington Galleries, 11 Cork Street, London W1S 3LT, **27**, Courtesy of Alan Cristea Gallery, 31 & 34 Cork Street, London W1S 3NU, **683**

Davey, Rose, 26 Ecclesbourne Road, London N1 3AE, **300**

Davey, Toni, Westmoor, North Hill Road, Minehead, Somerset TA24 5SF, **118**

David Kohn Architects, 511 Highgate Studios, 53-79 Highgate Road, London N19 5TZ, **1030**

Davidson, Colin, 2 Lowry Hill, Bangor, County Down BT19 1BX, **848, 855**

Davidson, Martin, 35 Elder Avenue, London N8 8PS, **532**

Davie, Alan, Courtesy of Open Eye Gallery, 34 Abercromby Place, Edinburgh EH3 6QE, **844, 875**

Davies, Richard, North Space, Salamander Court, 135 York Way, London N7 9LG, **894, 895**

Davis, Kate and David Moore, 56 Nelson Road, London N8 9RT, **1212**

Dawson, Stuart, 10 Gatehouse, Blackstone Edge Old Road, Littleborough, Lancashire OL15 0JJ, **1341**

de Cordova, Denise, 31 Sotheby Road, London N5 2UP, **1441**

DE GREY, Spencer, CBE RA, Foster + Partners, Riverside, 22 Hester Road, London SW11 4AN, **966, 1064, 1065**

de la Cruz, Angela, Courtesy of the Artist and Lisson Gallery, 52-54 Bell Street, London NW1 5BU, **819**

de Lannoy, Caroline, 10 Cricketfield Road, London E5 8NS, **356** de Monchaux, Cathy, 1 Hoxton Street, London N1 6NL, **238, 810**

de Monchaux, Paul, 56 Manor Avenue, London SE4 1TE, **837, 838**

de Monchaux, Ruth, 56 Manor Avenue, London SE4 1TE, **784, 785**

de Sade, Dolores, 10 Manse Road, London N16 7QD, **674**

de Waal, Edmund, Courtesy of Alan Cristea Gallery, 31 & 34 Cork Street, London W1S 3NU, **814**

DEACON, Richard, CBE RA, c/o Royal Academy of Arts, **1012**

Deakins, Tom, 31 The Causeway, Great Dunmow, Essex CM6 2AA, **364**

Dean, Mike, Wilkinson Eyre Architects, 33-39 Bowling Green Lane, London EC1R 0BJ, **973**

Deely, Neil, Metropolitan Workshop, 14-16 Cowcross Street, London EC1M 6DG, **971**

Dellow, Jeff, 92 Upper Brockley Road, London SE4 1ST, **227, 239**

Demetriou, Nicolas, 20 Miller House, Forster Road, London SW2 4UY, **320**

Dennis, Jeffrey, 94 Beaconsfield Road, London N15 4SQ, **278**

Denton, Bea, 91 Swallowfield Road, London SE7 7NT, **796**

Desborough, Jill, 13 Bourne Road, Colchester, Essex CO2 7LQ, **1191**

DESMET, Anne, RA, c/o Hart Gallery, 113 Upper Street, London N1 1QN, **641, 642, 643, 644, 645, 1071**

Devlin, Glenna, 37 Rochester Road, London NW1 9JJ, **699**

di Mascio, Fabiana, 6 Matson Road, Ipswich, Suffolk IP1 4ET, **206**

DICKSON, Dr Jennifer, RA, 20 Osborne Street, Ottawa, Ontario, K1S 4Z9, Canada, **788, 789, 790, 791, 793, 794**

Dilnot, John, Studio A, Level 2, New England House, New England Street, Brighton, East Sussex BN1 4GH, **802**

Dupré, Ruth, 18 Rectory Grove, London SW4 0EA, **1307**

DURRANT, Jennifer, RA, La Vigna, Via Bondi 14, Tuoro-Sul-Trasimeno, 6069, Italy, **39, 391, 926, 1359, 1402, 1422**

Dusheiko, Neil, 116 Nevill Road, London N16 0SX, **1060**

Dutton, Meg, 19 Morella Road, London SW12 8UQ, **664**

Dyson, Christopher, 11 Princelet Street, London E1 6QH, **1031, 1113**

E

Eason, Ewan David, 263 Kingsland Road, London E2 8AS, **755**

Eastman, Ken, Eaton Hennor, Hamnish, Leominster, Herefordshire HR6 0QN, **1274**

Easton, Bella, 40 Ruskin Walk, London SE24 9LZ, **728, 937**

Edmunds, Joanne Ruth, 33 Tria Apartments, 49 Durant Street, London E2 7DT, **975**

Edwards, Dave, Flat 23, Pemberton Gardens, London N19 5RT, **1026**

Edwards, Kim, Eastways, Middleton IP17 3NY, **233**

Eglin, Philip, 14 Heol Rheolau, Abercrave, Swansea, Wales SA9 1TE, **965, 1229**

Eisner, Robert, 70 Lake View, Edgware HA8 7RU, **61**

Elfick, Pennie, Calders, Stathe, Nr Bridgwater, Somerset TA7 0JN, **326**

Elliott, Rachel Mary, Unit 10, Castlebrae Business Centre, 40 Peffer Place, Edinburgh EH16 4BB, **1281**

Ellis, Belinda, St Mary's Lodge, Church Street, Bloxham, Oxon OX15 4ES, **612**

Elmes, Hilary, Roscat, Tullow, Co. Carlow, Ireland, **107**

EM2B Architects, 1 Thane Villas, Studio 103, London N7 7PH, **1038**

EMIN, Prof. Tracey, RA, 1 Tenter Ground, London E1 7NH, **569, 570, 572, 1446**

Evans, Brenda, Oystercatcher, 31 Beresford Road, Whitstable, Kent CT5 1JP, **86**

Evans, Mary-Jane, Flat 4, 1 Great Bedford Street, Bath, Somerset BA12TZ, **1309**

Evans, Michael, Old White Horse, Francis Road, Ware, Hertfordshire, SG12 9HA, **700**

EYTON, Anthony, RA, c/o Browse and Darby, 19 Cork Street, London W1S 3LP, **414, 882, 884, 1396, 1397, 1419**

F

Faine, Bradley, c/o CCA Galleries, Greenhills Estate, Tilford Road, Tilford GU10 2DZ, **681**

Farago, Leslie, 13B Greenland Road, London NW1 0AX, **58**

Farley, Lucy Kristiane, 324A Portobello Road, London W10 5RU, **742**

FARTHING, Prof. Stephen, RA, Chelsea School of Art, 16 John Islip Street, London SW1P 4JU, **457, 462, 1326, 1442**

Fathers, Olly, 3 Shannon Grove, London SW9 8BY, **193, 493**

Fay, Helen, Hawthorn House, Whittingham, Nr Alnwick, Northumberland NE66 4UW, **693**

Feakins, Chris, 24 Pickhurst Park, Bromley, Kent BR2 0UF, **339**

Featherstone, Sarah, Featherstone Young, 25 Links Yard, Spelman Street, London E1 5LX, **1070, 1148**

FEDDEN, Mary, OBE RA PPRWA, Portland Gallery, 8 Bennet Street, London SW1A 1RP, **431**

Feinson, Nadine, 3 Juggs Close, Lewes, East Sussex BN7 1QP, **336**

Fenn, Alison, 342 Station Road, Knowle, Solihull B93 0ET, **898**

Fennell, Lance, 1 Hedingham Court, Shenley Church End, Milton Keynes MK5 6HP, **200**

Ferguson, Catherine, 23 Cockburn House, Aylesford Street, London SW1V 3RT, **1391**

Ferrand Scott, Victoria, Field Head, Leeds Road, Smaws, Nr Tadcaster, North Yorkshire LS24 9LP, **1287**

Ferris, Steve, 89 Lambs Lane, Cottenham, Cambridge CB24 8TB, **109**

Fisher, James, Eagle Gallery, 159 Farringdon Road, London EC1R 3AL, **1447, 1448**

Fitzmaurice, John, 129A Newington Green Road, London
NI 4RA, **23**

Flea Folly Ltd, c/o Pascal Bronner, Flat 6, Piano Factory,
36-38 Peckham Road, London SE5 8GB, **1128**

Flynn, James and Clayton, Ashley, Flat 20,
Northumberland House, 237 Ballards Lane, Finchley
Church End, London N3 1LB, **1029**

Foggo Associates, 55 Charterhouse Street, London
ECIM 6PR, **1140**

Forrest, Teresa, Malthouse Barn, The Maltings, Sibford
Road, Hook Norton OX15 5JZ, **186**

FOSTER OF THAMES BANK, Lord, OM RA,
Foster + Partners, Riverside, 22 Hester Road, London
SWII 4AN, **992, 993**

Fowler, Jaana, 42 Winton Avenue, London NII 2AT, **1200**

Franks, Stuart, 27 Overstone Road, Flat 4, London
W6 OAD, **1046**

Frazer, David, c/o Rebecca Hossack Gallery, 2A Conway
Street, London WIT 6BA, **716**

FREETH, Peter, RA, 83 Muswell Hill Road, London
NIO 3HT, **622, 623, 624, 625, 626, 632**

Frith, Ed, 40 Clarence Mews, London E5 8HL, **915**

Fudge, Z. E., 127 Poynton Road, London NI7 9SJ, **1069**

Furneaux, Paul, 36 Rodney Street (2f1), Edinburgh
EH7 4DX, **1263**

Furniss, Darren, 6 Tumbling Close, Wakefield, West
Yorkshire WF5 OQX, **1068**

G

Gabbitas, Jarrod, 6 Holywell Terrace, Abbey Foregate,
Shrewsbury SY2 5DF, **332**

Garfen, Caren, 15 Hillview Road, London NW7 1AJ, **230**

Garrido Molina, José Manuel, 9 Pekin Street, London
EI4 6EZ, **1072**

Gatenby, Timothy, 180 Beechcroft Road, London
SWI7 7DG, **168**

Genestine-Charlton, Greg, 66 Ackroyd Drive, London
E3 4JX, **400**

Genovés, Ana, Flat 11, Bruno Court, 10 Fassett Square, London E8 1BF, **1196, 1245**

George, Patrick, Courtesy of Browse & Darby, London, **830, 831**

Georgi, Meike, Friedrich Engels Str. 60, Zwickau 08058, Germany **604**

Gharbawi, Mohammed, 21 Onslow Gardens, London SW7 3AL, **189, 208**

Ghose, Maximilian, 32 South Eaton Place, London SW1W 9JJ, **185**

Gibbons, Jeff, 123A Evering Road, London N16 7BU, **197**

Gibbs, Stephen, 11 Stanfield Road, Southend-on-Sea, Essex SS2 5DQ, **772**

Gilani, Rani, 15½ Jackson's Lane, London N6 5SR, **81**

Giles, Lucy, 5A Thorn Terrace, Nunhead Grove, London SE15 3LN, **151**

Gillespie, Sarah, Clover Cottage, Blackawton, Totnes, Devon TQ9 7BN, **167, 892**

Girling, Sheila, 111 Frognal, London NW3 6XR, **52**

Glendinning, Lucy, Welham Studios, Charlton Mackrell, Somerset TA11 7AJ, **1272**

Goldwyn-Simpkins, Eva, 50 Whitelow Road, Chorlton, Manchester M21 9HR, **551**

Gooding, Edward, 70 Hall Tower, Hall Place, London W2 1LW, **365**

Goodwin, Marc, 33 Campbell Road, Caterham, Surrey CR3 5JP, **207**

Gough, Lucy, c/o Jealous Gallery, 27 Park Road, London Middlesex, N8 8TE, **690**

GOUGH, Piers, CBE RA, CZWG Architects LLP, 17 Bowling Green Lane, London EC1R 0QB, **1033, 1049**

Gould, David, 30 Waterloo Road, Cardiff CF23 5AE, **25**

Grasset, Aude, 15 Ladbroke Square, London W11 3NA, **87, 156**

Gray, Euan, 20/4 Spittal Street, Edinburgh EH3 9DT, **858, 866**

GREEN, Anthony, RA, c/o Whitcombe Associates,
62 Cloncurry Street, London sw6 6DU, **265, 450, 547,
550, 1361**

Greenall, Tom and Jordan Hodgson, 87 Columbia Road,
London E2 7RG, **1155**

Greig, Neal, Seveagh, Glaslough, Co. Monaghan, Ireland,
889

Griffiths, Rebecca, Flat 60, Goulden House, Bullen
Street, London sw11 3HG, **1266, 1288**

Grigor, Rachel, 135 Wollaton Vale, Nottingham,
Nottinghamshire, NG8 2PE, **721**

GRIMSHAW, Sir Nicholas, CBE PPRA, 57 Clerkenwell
Road, London ECIM 5NG, **571, 969**

Grocott, Robert, Stockman's Cottage, Clattinger Farm,
Oaksey, Nr. Malmesbury, Wiltshire sn16 9TW,
1276

Grover, Martin, Flat 2, 31 Morrish Road, London sw2 4EB,
260

Guilhem, Carles, 95 Rue Fabre d'Eglantine, Montpellier,
34070, France, **1308**

Gurbuz, Selma, c/o Rose Issa Projects, 269 Kensington
High Street, London w8 6NA, **110, 913**

Gutch, Juliet and Jamie, 25 Lister Street, Ilkley, West
Yorkshire ls29 9ET, **1199**

Gutsche, Claas, Freienwalder Strasse 14, Berlin, 13055,
Germany, **521**

H

Hackney, Tom, 58A Elderfield Road, London E5 0LF, **302,
398**

HADID, Zaha, CBE RA, Zaha Hadid Architecture, Studio
9, 10 Bowling Green Lane, London ECIR 0BQ, **998, 999,
1000**

Hadzi-Vasileva, Elpida, 18 Stanley Road, Brighton
BN1 4NJ, **1208**

Halford, Caro, 13 Palewell Park, London sw14 8JQ, **701**

Hall, Robin-Lee, 40 Romans Way, Pyrford, Woking
GU22 8TR, **148**

HALL, Nigel, RA, 11 Kensington Park Gardens, London W11 3HD, **1251, 1300, 1331**

Hallam, Marilyn, Lower Flat, 55 Marischal Road, London SE13 5LE, **53, 891**

Hammick, Tom, The Eagle Gallery, 159 Farringdon Road, London EC1A 3AL, **438**, West Beam, Henley Down, Battle, East Sussex TN33 9BN, **574**

Hampson, Mark, 16 Dickens Road, Broadstairs, Kent CT10 1DX, **740**

Hanley, Hilary, 21 Woodsome Road, London NW5 1RX, **698**

Hanselaar, Marcelle, 58 Eccleston Square, London SW1V1PH, **808**

Harding, Jennifer, 57 Reardon House, Reardon Street, Wapping, London E1W 2QJ, **181**

Harding, Alexis, c/o University of East London ADI, 4-6 University Way, London E16 2RD, **435**

Hargreaves, Barton, 34 Shrewsbury Lane, Shooters Hill, London SE18 3JF, **630, 758**

Harild, Anne, 77 Beulah Road, London E17 9LD, **299**

Harley, Alexandra, 182 Downhills Park Road, London N17 6AP, **1227**

Harris, Jane, Grelière, Nanthiat, 24800, France, **166, 1385**

Hart, Maxine, The Stennings, Chalbury Heights, Brill, Falmouth, Cornwall TR11 5UR, **216**

Hart, Paul, Walnut House, Somerby Road, Ropsley, Nr Grantham, Lincolnshire, NG33 4AZ, **541**

Hassan, Fathi, c/o Rose Issa Projects, 269 Kensington High Street, London W8 6NA, **152, 1421**

Hawdon, Paul, 9 Worts Causeway, Cambridge CB1 8RJ, **631, 778**

Hawkins\Brown Ltd, c/o Nicole Woodman, 60 Bastwick Street, London EC1V 3TN, **1116, 1132**

Hawser, Eloise, Unit 222, 30 Great Guildford Street, London SE1 0HS, **1195, 1197**

Haynes, Kate, The Old Butchers Shop, The Street, Shurlock Row, Berkshire RG10 0PS, **418**

Head, Tim, 129 Camden Mews, London NW1 9AH, **812, 813**

Hebson, Nadia, 2E King Street, Newcastle Upon Tyne NE1 3UQ, **112, 223**

Hedayati, Mohammad Daud, Turquoise Mountain Institute, House # 300 & 301, District 2 Murad Khani, Behind Ministry of Finance, Kabul, Afghanistan, **98**

Hefuna, Susan, c/o Rose Issa Projects, 269 Kensington High Street, London W8 6NA, **137**

Heller, Rachel, c/o Flowers Gallery, 82 Kingsland Road, London E2 8DP, **73, 1340**

Hellman, Louis, 6 Montague Gardens, Acton, London W3 9PT, **1084, 1085**

He.Lo Architects LLP, 60 Tennyson Road, London NW6 7SA, **1061**

Hemami, Taraneh, c/o Rose Issa Projects, 269 Kensington High Street, London W8 6NA, **198, 199**

Hempton, Celia, First Floor Flat, 34 Albert Road, London N4 3RW, **117, 351**

Hemsworth, Gerard, Blacklands, 28 Hughenden Road, Hastings, East Sussex TN34 3TG, **1390**

Henegan Barr, Geraldine, 12 Pinfold Lane, Stapleford, Nottinghamshire NG9 8DL, **1205**

Henningham Family Press, 130 Sandringham Road, London E8 2HJ, **702**

Hensler, David, Penny Cottage, The Green, Newick, East Sussex BN8 4LA, **350**

Heron, Susanna, 9 Gibraltar Walk, London E2 7LH, **1249**

Hesamiyan, Sahand, No.7, Apartment 4, Yas Ct, Shahid Soori Street, Evin, Chamran High, Tehran, 1997657557, Iran, **1190**

Hewitt, John, 11 Harrop Green, Diggle, Saddleworth, Oldham, OL3 5LW, **544**

Hicklin, Jason, c/o Beardsmore Gallery, 22-24 Prince of Wales Road, London NW5 3LG, **618, 901**

Hicks, Nicola, c/o Flowers Gallery, 82 Kingsland Road, London E2 8DP, **1265**

Hiles, Adam, Flat 4, Heritage House, 1 Marlowe Avenue, Canterbury, Kent CT1 2QN, **1101, 1102**

Hill, Alexander, Flat 5 Bombay Court, 59 St Marychurch Street, London SE16 4HW, **1097, 1103**

Hipkiss, Paul, 37 The Crescent, Cradley Heath, West Midlands B64 7JS, **899**

Hiscock, Simon, 47 Iliffe Street, London SE17 3LJ, **815**

Hobbs, Jim, 30 Linden Grove, London SE15 3LF, **525**

Hobson, Laurence, 110 High Street, Chesterton, Cambridge CB4 1NW, **353**

Holl, Steven, 450 West 31st Street, 11th floor, New York, NY, USA, **1086, 1087**

Hopkins, Clyde, c/o Advanced Graphics, 32 Long Lane, London SE1 4AY, **195**

HOPKINS, Sir Michael, CBE RA, Hopkins Architects, 27 Broadley Terrace, London NW1 6LG, **1005, 1107, 1159**

Horakhsh, Nabila, c/o Turquoise Mountain Institute, House # 300 & 301, District 2 Murad Khani, Behind Ministry of Finance, Kabul, Afghanistan, **99**

Horner, Marguerite, 65 Rusthall Avenue, London W4 1BN, **221**

Houshiary, Shirazeh, Courtesy of the Artist and Lisson Gallery, 52-54 Bell Street, London NW1 5DA, **836**

Houston, Adrian, 43 Aldbourne Road, London W12 0LW, **905**

HOWARD, Ken, OBE RA, Richard Green Gallery, 147 New Bond Street, London W1S 2TS, **8, 460, 488, 887, 1367, 1414**

Howard, Rachel, 16 Albert Square, London SW8 1BS, **254, 416**

Hoyland, The late John, RA, c/o Royal Academy of Arts, **17, 18**

Hubbard, Steven, 1 Berkeley Villas, Lower Street, Stroud GL5 2HU, **736**

Hudson, Alex, 42c Kyverdale Road, London N16 7AH, **66, 228**

Hughes, Alexandra, 32 Kelshall Court, Brownswood Road, London N4 2XJ, **183, 242**

Hughes, Pauline, 15 Orchard Hey, Old Roan, Liverpool L30 8RX, **1302**

Hugonin, James, Courtesy of the Artist and Ingleby Gallery, 15 Calton Road, Edinburgh EH8 8DL, **317**

HUME, Gary, RA, c/o Royal Academy of Arts, **1440**

Humphreys, David, Maudlin Hill House, Sopers Lane, Steyning, West Sussex BN44 3PU, **897, 960**

Hunter, Kenny, Unit M, 7 Craigend Place, Glasgow G13 2UN, **880**, Courtesy of Inspired Editions, **881**

Hutton, Julia, Front Room Studio, 110 South Street, Bridport, Dorset DT6 3NW, **180**

HUXLEY, Prof. Paul, RA, 2 Dalling Road, London W6 0JB, **290, 291, 1357**

Hwang, Ilsu, 9 Tomline House, Union Street, London SE1 0ET, **483**

HYMAN, Timothy, RA, 62 Myddelton Square, London EC1R 1XX, **21, 22, 187, 442, 765, 1410**

Hymas, Anna, 9 Brett Close, London N16 0BN, **64**

I

Innes, Callum, Courtesy of the Artist and Frith Street Gallery, 17-18 Golden Square , London W1F 9JJ, **870**

IRVIN, Albert, RA, c/o Gimpel Fils, 30 Davies Street, London W1K 4NB, **245, 333, 375, 1368**, c/o Advanced Graphics, 32 Long Lane, London SE1 4AY, **685, 686**

Isgar, Caroline, 6 Friendly Street, London SE8 4DT, **712, 713**

Ive, Martin, 57 East Smithfield, London E1W 1AW, **360**

J

JACKLIN, Bill, RA, c/o Marlborough Fine Art Ltd, 6 Albemarle Street, London W1S 4BY, **519, 520, 524, 594, 942, 1449**

Jackowski, Andrzej, Courtesy of Purdy Hicks Gallery, 65 Hopton Street, London SE1 9GZ, **295, 1324**

Jackson, Vanessa, 169 Bermondsey Street, London SE1 3UW, **627, 628**

James, Jeffrey, 11 Atlas Mews, Dalston, London E8 2NE,
1021

Jaques, Stephen, Flat 2, 34 Belvedere Road, London
SE19 2HW, **471**

JARAY, Tess, RA, 29 Camden Square, London NW1 9XA,
305, 826, 827, Courtesy of Advanced Graphics, 32 Long
Lane, London SE1 4AY, **684**

Jay, Nimal, Clonattin, Ermyn Way, Leatherhead, Surrey
KT22 8TW, **1234**

Jeffries, Neil, 40 Allfarthing Lane, London SW18 2AJ, **100,
284**

Jessop, Effie, 4 Hemdean Rise, Caversham, Reading,
Berks RG4 7SA, **190**

JIRICNA, Eva, CBE RA, Eva Jiricna Architects Ltd, Third
Floor, 38 Warren Street, London W1T 6AE, **1032, 1034**

Joffe, Jasper, Unit 3, 7A Plough Yard, London EC2A 3LP,
285

John McAslan + Partners, 7–9 William Road, London
NW1 3ER, **1062, 1063**

Johnson, Philippa, 144B Deptford High Street, London
SE8 3PQ, **1452**

Johnson Soliz, Cecile, 166 Kings Road, Cardiff CF11 9DG,
1253

Jokhova, Evy, 6 Dresden Road, London N19 3BD, **805**

JONES, Allen, RA, 41 Charterhouse Square, London
EC1M 6EA, **363, 1371**

Jones, Katherine, 34 Crownstone Court, Crownstone
Road, London SW2 1LS, **500, 774**

Jones, Lucy, c/o Flowers Gallery, 82 Kingsland Road,
London E2 8DP, **203**

Jones, Morgan, 'Whakatipua', PO Box 36, Arrowtown,
9351, New Zealand, **1173**

Jones, Mulberry, 22 Queen Anne's Place, Enfield EN1 2PT,
1353

Jones, Neal, 32B Elder Avenue, London N8 8PS, **240, 264**

Jones, Patrick Adam, Garden Flat, 11 Church Road,
St Leonards on Sea, Sussex TN37 6EF, **179**

Judge, James, 39 Leighton Avenue, Leigh on Sea, Essex SS9 1QB, **139**

Julareesuk, Hathaichanok, Flat 2, Elephant and Castle Pub, 119 Newington Causeway, London SE1 6BN, **1464**

Julian Harrap Architects, 95 Kingsland Road, London E2 8AG, **1079**

Junghanns, Christian, Mars Strasse 13, Munich, D80335, Germany, **1394**

K

Kalkhof, Peter, Courtesy of the Artist and Annely Juda Fine Art, 23 Dering Street, London W1S 1AW, **286**

Kander, Nadav, c/o Flowers Gallery, 82 Kingsland Road, London E2 8DP, **893, 1467**

Kang, Seokyeong, 15 Petersham Mews, London SW7 5NR, **124**

Karpati, Eszter, Basement Flat, 19A Gibson Square, London N1 ORD, **1352**

Karunaratne, Gihan, 80 Beaconsfield Road, London SE3 7LQ, **919**

Keith Williams Architects, 17-21 Emerald Street, London WC1N 3QN, **1037, 1091**

Kelly, Jane, The Garden Flat, 5 Larden Road, London W3 7ST, **1345**

Kennedy, Eddie, Courtesy of the Artist and Hillsboro Fine Art, 49 Parnell Square West, Dublin 1, Ireland, **850, 953**

Kennedy, Michael, 107 Knights Croft, New Ash Green, Longfield, Kent DA3 8HY, **141**

KERR, Janette, PRWA Hon Member Ex Officio, Hill House, Church Street, Coleford, Nr Radstock, Somerset BA3 5NA, **456**

Kha, Caroline, 29C Islip Street, London NW5 2DJ, **301**

Khorsand, Guitty, 81 Fountains Crescent, London N14 6BD, **909**

Kidd, Natasha, 79 Observatory Street, Oxford OX2 6EP, **219**

KIEFER, Anselm, Hon RA, Courtesy of the Artist and White Cube, 48 Hoxton Square, London N1 6PB, **824**

Kiely, Frank, Studio UN13, 235-241 Union Street, London SE21 0LR, **771**

Kihara, Yoshimi, 18 Woodriffe Road, London E11 1AH, **1222**

Kikuma, Yuichiro, Flat 5, 137 Arthur Road, London SW19 8AB, **920**

Kim, Hayoung, 13 Regency Court, 55 Hartfield Road, London SW19 3SF, **318**

Kim, Jieun, 91G Breakspears Road, London SE4 1TX, **1465**

Kimber, Max, Old Way House, Moat Lane, Fordwich, Canterbury, Kent CT2 0DP, **1289**

King, Alastair, 29 Beaver Close, Horsham, West Sussex RH12 5GB, **1047**

KING, Prof. Phillip, CBE PPRA, 26 Savernake Road, London NW3 2JP, **734, 1429, 1430, 1431, 1432, 1433**

Kirwan, Richard, 72 Sandmere Road, London SW4 7QH, **689**

Kitching, Alan, c/o Advanced Graphics, 32 Long Lane, London SE1 4AY, **737**

Klein, Anita, c/o Advanced Graphics, 32 Long Lane, London SE1 4AY, **722**

Klein, Jochen, 86 Donnington Court, Donnington Road, London NW10 3TJ, **1453**

KNEALE, Prof. Bryan, RA, 10A Muswell Road, London N10 2BG, **963, 1217, 1218, 1219, 1220, 1221**

Knight-Webb, Rufus, 47 Beckwith Road, London SE24 9LQ, **407**

Kogan, Gillian, 2 St Thomas Gardens, London NW5 4EX, **617**

Kolakowski, Matthew, 166 Brixton Road, London SW9 6AU, **259**

Kondracki, Henry, 20 Marchmont Crescent, Edinburgh EH9 1HL, **957**

KORALEK, Paul, CBE RA, 3 Rochester Road, London NW1 9JH, **986, 987, 988, 989, 990, 991**

Korzer-Robinson, Alexander, 37 Philip Street, Bristol BS3 4EA, **523**

Kotrba, Tadeas, Bezrvcova 801, Roznov Pod, Radhostem, 75661, Czech Republic, **376**

Kubecki, Terry, 66 Barrett Road, London E17 9ET, **610**

Levy, Valeria, 12 Elsworthy Road, London NW3 3DJ, **340**

Lewis, Elfyn, 9 Bradford Street, Cardiff CF11 7BZ, **65, 443**

Lewis, Stephen, 76 Royal Hill, London SE10 8RT, **1214**

Li, Na, 30 Maha Building, Merchant Street, London E3 4PZ, **1010, 1011**

Liddicoat & Goldhill Architects, White Lodge, Monken Hadley, Barnet EN5 5PY, **1130**

Lifschutz Davidson Sandilands, Island Studios, 22 St Peter's Square, London W6 9NW, **1096, 1153**

Lijn, Liliane, 93 Vale Road, London N4 1TG, **1258**

Lintine, David, 79A Leigham Court Drive, Leigh-on-Sea, Essex SS9 1PT, **775**

Locke, Lana, First Floor, 5 North Pole Road, London W10 6QH, **1235**

Lomas, Greg, Unit 1, 14 Weller Street, London SE1 1QU, **964**

Lomax, Tom, 6 Friendly Street, London SE8 4DT, **394, 820**

Long, Fiona, 65 Lyveden Road, London SW17 9DT, **96**

Long, Tim, 60 Salisbury Road, Canterbury, Kent CT27HH, **1248**

Longkumer, Temsuyanger, Flat 2, 11A White Church Lane, London E1 7QR, **1244**

Lord, Nigel, 2 Dairy Cottages, Briantspuddle, Dorchester, Dorset DT2 7HT, **1460**

Low, Sharon, 39 St Clairs Road, Croydon, Surrey CR0 5NE, **694**

Lowe, Francesca, 25D Queensdown Road, London E5 8NN, **159**

Lowe, Jeff, The Red Wing, 6A Havelock Walk, London SE233 HG, **1198**

Lushington, Juliet, 22 Collinson Walk, London SE1 1PU, **475, 495**

Lykiard, Suzanne, 41 Yew Tree Bottom Road, Epsom Downs, Surrey KT17 3NQ, **123**

Lynch Architects Ltd, 1 Amwell Street, London EC1R 1UL, **1077**

M

Macalpine, Jean, Carrer Gran 55A, Es Castell, Menorca, 7720, Spain, **669, 792**

MacCarthy, Katharine, 22 St Paul's Place, London N1 2QF, **1296**

MacColl, Eòghann, The Hill, Dunlop, Kilmarnock, East Ayrshire KA3 4DH, **923**

MacEwan, Jane, Capel House, Badminton, Gloucestershire GL9 1DG, **421**

MACH, Prof. David, RA, 8 Havelock Walk, London SE23 3HG, **878, 1164, 1165, 1189**

Mackechnie, John, 6 Holyrood Crescent, Glasgow G20 6HJ, **671**

Maclean, Will, 18 Dougall Street, Tayport, Fife DD6 9JD, **864, 872**

MacPhee, Marion, Flat 3/2, 191 Hyndland Road, Glasgow G12 9HT, **675**

Madgwick, Lee, 4 Churchill Close, Ely, Cambridgeshire CB6 3BT, **119, 933**

Magill, Elizabeth, Acme Studios, 15-31 Orsman Road, London N1 5RA, **787**

Mahony, Louisa, 4 Wingmore Road, London SE24 0AS, **399**

MAINE, John, RA, Former School, Church Road, East Knoyle, Salisbury, Wiltshire SP3 6AE, **1225, 1423, 1424, 1425, 1426, 1427**

Mainwaring, Robert, 72 Gudge Heath Lane, Fareham, Hampshire PO15 5AY, **1114, 1115**

Make Architects, 55 Whitfield Street, London W1T 4AH, **1143, 1156**

Makower, Noah, 85 Hartington Road, London W4 3TU, **423**

Malina, Karimi, c/o Turquoise Mountain Institute, House # 300 & 301, District 2 Murad Khani, Behind Ministry of Finance, Kabul, Afghanistan, **88**

Malla, Dijan, 113 Myddleton Avenue, London N4 2FN **984**

MANASSEH, Leonard, OBE RA PPRWA, 6 Bacon's Lane, Highgate Village, London N6 6BL, **1050, 1052, 1073, 1075, 1076, 1081**

MANSER, Michael, CBE RA PPRIBA Hon RAIC, The Manser Practice, Bridge Studios, Hammersmith Bridge Road, London W6 9DA, **1055, 1056**

Mansfield, Andrew, Anthony Reynolds Gallery, 60 Great Marlborough Street, London W1F 7BG, **1356**

Marinkov, Sasa, Woodcut, Riverside, Twickenham TW1 3DJ, **666**

Markides, Christos, Flat 3, 228 Uxbridge Road, London W12 7JD, **1058**

Marks Barfield Architects, 50 Bromells Road, London SW4 0BG, **917**

Marsh, Peter, 8A Newmarket Road, Brighton, East Sussex BN2 3QF, **426**

Martin, Ruth, Studio 311, Cockpit Arts, 18-22 Creekside, London SE8 3DZ, **806**

Martin, Sonia, 63B Kennington Park Road, London SE11 4JQ, **767, 773**

Martina, Toni, 85 Harold Road, Hastings, East Sussex TN35 5NJ, **752**

Matthews, Emma-Kate, 99 Lansdowne Way, London SW8 2BP, **1041**

Matthews, Francis, 19 Woodfield Ice, Inchicore, Dublin 8, Ireland, **433**

McBeath, Norman, 4 Learmonth Gardens Mews, Edinburgh EH4 1EX, **868**

McCabe, Pauline, 7 Orchard Rise, Burford, OX18 4SZ, **138**

McCausland, Onya, 30 Dartmouth Park Hill, London NW5 1HL, **272, 825**

McClarey, Louise, c/o Adam Gallery, 24 Cork Street, London W1S 3NJ, **26**

McClure, Calum, 2F3, 123 Nicolson Street, Edinburgh EH8 9ER, **853, 854**

Miller, Michael, 22 Court Farm Avenue, Ewell, Surrey
  KT19 0HF, **371**
MILROY, Lisa, RA, Courtesy of Alan Cristea Gallery,
  31 & 34 Cork Street, London W1S 3NU, **1333, 1334, 1335**
MISTRY, Prof. Dhruva, CBE RA, Grosvenor Gallery,
  21 Ryder Street, London SW1Y 6PX, **1434, 1435**
Mitchell, Julian, 57 Knox Green, Binfield, Berkshire,
  RG42 4NZ, **106, 479**
Mitchell, Sarah Ann, 7 Norlington Road, London E11 4BE,
  395
Mixity Design Ltd, Cambridge House, 100 Cambridge
  Grove, London W6 0LE, **1118**
Mojadidi, Aman, c/o Galerie Nikki Diana Marquardt,
  9 Place des Vosges, 75004 Paris, France, **277**
Monroe, Chuck, 26 Albany Road, London E17 8DA, **411**
Moon, Christopher, 40 George Road, New Malden,
  KT36BU, **1466**
MOON, Mick, RA, Courtesy of Alan Cristea Gallery,
  31 & 34 Cork Street, London W1S 3NU, **1398**
Moore, David, Davis, Kate, 56 Nelson Road, London
  N8 4RT
Morey de Morand, Colette, 61D Oxford Gardens,
  London W10 5UJ, **246, 247**
Morgan, Jane, 45 Bridewell Place, London E1W 2PB, **1211**
Morling, Katharine, Studio 205, 18-22 Creekside, London
  SE8 3DZ, **1201, 1202**
Morris, Andrew, 28 Rushcroft Road, High Crompton,
  Shaw, Oldham, OL2 7PR, **1092**
Morris, Annie, 59 Cross Street, London N1 2BB, **191, 835**
MORRIS, Mali, RA, APT Studios, Harold Wharf, 6
  Creekside, London SE8 4SA, **10, 276, 409, 410, 1320, 1387**
Morrison, Alex Gene, Basement Flat, 287 Glyn Road,
  London E5 0JP, **472, 1382**
Mosley, Ryan, Courtesy of the Artist and Alison Jacques
  Gallery, London, **1329**
Moxhay, Suzanne, 36 Woodham Drive, Hatfield Peverel,
  Chelmsford, Essex CM3 2RR, **636, 648**

Moye and Young, Robert and Peter, 87 Richmond Road, London E11 4BT, **1456**

Muchemwa, Bongani Elton, 38 Stafford Venue, Norwich, Norfolk NR5 0QE, **1045**

Münster, Jost, 94 Greenwood Road, London E8 1NE, **153**

N

Naor, Esther, 1 Hashikma Street, P.o.b 8, 56530 Savion, Israel, **1262**

Narita, Miyako, 18B Ashby Street, London EC1V 0ED, **1339**

NASH, David, OBE RA, c/o Annely Juda Fine Art, 23 Dering Street, London W1S 1AW, **1269**

Naughten, Jim, Spes, Victoria Steps Quay, Kewbridge, Brentford, Middlesex TW8 0DX, **1344, 1469**

Naylor, Philip, 16 Penwerris Terrace, Falmouth, Cornwall TR11 2PA, **513**

Negus, Susanna, 5 Ladies Mile Road, Brighton, East Sussex BN1 8QE, **218, 343**

Neiland, Brendan, c/o The Redfern Gallery, 20 Cork Street, London W1S 3HL, **667, 925**

Newling, John, 91 Watcombe Circus, Nottingham NG5 2DU, **307**

Newsome, Victor, c/o The Grosvenor Gallery, 21 Ryder Street, London SW1Y 6PX, **345**

Ng, Geraldine, 20 Grove Lane, London SE5 8ST, **979**

Ng, James, Flat No. 1, 1st Floor, 2B Kings Cross Road, London WC1X 9QA, **357**

Niall McLaughlin Architects, c/o Bryony Jones, 39-51 Highgate Road, London NW5 1RS, **1036**

Nicholas Hare Architects, c/o Mona Heier, 3 Barnsbury Square, London N1 1JL, **1124**

Nicolas, Francisco, Studio 605, 128 Blackfriars Road, London SE1 8EQ, **362**

Nishihata, Alexis, Flat 7, Poets Court, 52 Churchfield Road, London W3 6DA, **325**

Nix, Marianne, 9 Heath Villas, Vale of Health, London
NW3 1AW, **720**

Nixon, Louis, 21D St Michael's Road, London SW9 0SN,
158, 287

Noori, Yalda, c/o Turquoise Mountain Institute, House #
300 & 301, District 2 Murad Khani, Behind Ministry of
Finance, Kabul, Afghanistan, **80**

Nørkjær, Maria Bjerg, Weidekampsgade 55, 4.th,
Copenhagen S, 2300, Denmark, **941**

Nove-Josserand, Flore, Milcote House, Milcote Street,
London SE1 0RX, **220**

Nozkowski, Thomas, Courtesy of the Artist and Pace
Gallery, Liberty House, 222 Regents Street, London
W1B 5TR, **1388**

Nyee Macki, Eugène, 35 Elham House, Pembury Road,
London E5 8LT, **1207**

O   Oakley, Jo, Stable Cottage, 1½ Micheldever Road, London
SE12 8LX, **268**

Oates, David, 10 Worcester House, Astey's Row, London
N1 2DB, **1399**

OCEAN, Humphrey, RA, 22 Marmora Road, London
SE22 0RX, **832, 833, 834, 1319, 1403**

O'Connor, Grace, 15 Elaine Grove, London NW5 4QG, **412**

O'DONOGHUE, Hughie, RA, courtesy of Marlborough
Fine Art Ltd, 6 Albemarle Street, London W1S 4BY, **662,
663, 846, 862**

O'Donovan, Nuala, 4 Hollymount House, Lee Road,
Cork, Ireland, **1278**

Okore, Nnenna, October Gallery, 24 Old Gloucester
Street, London WC1N 3AL, **211**

Oldfield, Vicky, 7 Wessex Close, Thames Ditton, Surrey
KT7 0EJ, **557**

Olding, Alexandra, 4 Capel Close, Akeley, Buckingham
MK18 5HX, **697**

Olmos Zunica, Maria, Flat 10, 3 Elisa Court, Chitty
Street, London W1T 4AT, **1100**

Ommalbanin Hassani, Shamsia, c/o Turquoise Mountain Institute, House # 300 & 301, District 2 Murad Khani, Behind Ministry of Finance, Kabul, Afghanistan, **315**

O'Neill, Nigel, 20 Chancery House, Lowood Street, London E1 0BU, **226**

Opie, Julian, courtesy of Alan Cristea Gallery, 31 & 34 Cork Street, London W1S 3NU, **589**

O'Reilly, Michael, 42 Thackeray Court, Blythe Road, London W14 0PW, **224**

O'Reilly, Tom, The Bothy, Old Quay Lane, St Germans, Cornwall PL12 5LH, **809**

O'Rourke, Mark, 165 Elderfield Road, London E5 0AY, **12**

ORR, Prof. Chris, MBE RA, 5 Anhalt Road, London SW11 4NZ, **536, 537, 542, 543, 745, 1408**

Osipova, Viktorija, 11 Burgess Road, London E15 2AD, **615**

Ospina, Alejandro, 34B Albion Road, London N16 9PH, **253**

The Oval Partnership Architecture Ltd, Unit 206, 24-28 Hatton Wall, London EC1N 8JH, **1150**

Owusu-Ankomah, c/o October Gallery, 24 Old Gloucester Street, London WC1N 3AL, **108**

P   PALADINO, Mimmo, Hon RA, Courtesy of Alan Cristea Gallery, 31 & 34 Cork Street, London W1S 3NU, **549**, Artist's Private Collection, **1321**

Palumbi, Lidia, Oranje Nassaulaan 23, s Hertogenbosch, Netherlands 5211 AT, **1246**

PARKER, Cornelia, OBE RA, Courtesy of the Artist and Frith Street Gallery, London, **816, 821, 822, 823, 1271**

Parker, Jayne, 32 Elaine Grove, London NW5 4QH, **841, 842**

Parr, Tim, 36 Mendip Houses, Welwyn Street, London E2 0JW, **911**

PARRY, Eric, RA, Eric Parry Architects, 28-42 Banner Street, London EC1Y 8QE, **974, 1129**

Parry, Jackie, 3/2, 23 Kelvinside Gardens East, Glasgow G20 6BE, **573**

Piercy & Company, c/o Stephanie Wilkins, 5th Floor, 70-74 City Road, London EC1Y 2BJ, **1133**

Pilkington, Alison, 25 Montpelier Gardens, Dublin 7, Ireland, **393**

Pilkington, Cathie, 16 Steeple Court, Coventry Road, London E1 5QZ, **1292, 1295**

Pincis, Kasper, Flat 2, 80 Deptford High Street, London SE8 4RT, **178, 184**

Pirkis, Sarah, Butley Mills Studios, Mill Lane, Butley, Suffolk IP12 3PZ, **695**

Pockets, Danny, 19 Cloudesley Road, St Leonards-on-Sea, East Sussex TN37 6JW, **60**

Poncelet, Jacqueline, Flat A 117 Bellenden Road, London SE15 4QY, **1043, 1074**

Posner, Charlotte, 12 Newnham Close, Loughton, Essex IG10 4JG, **396**

Pragnell, Dizzy, Little Winchcombe, Crundale, Canterbury, Kent CT4 7EW, **801**

Priestley, Chris, 10 Albert Street, Cambridge, Cambridgeshire, CB4 3BE, **951**

Punch, Lara, 35 Docklewell Close, Towcester, Northamptonshire NN12 6JF, **386**

Q Quadrat, Simon, 9 Ivywell Road, Bristol BS9 1NX, **499**

R Rackowe, Nathaniel, Studio Rackowe, Bouverie Mews, London N16 0AE, **434**

RAE, Dr Barbara, CBE RA, c/o CCA Galleries, The Studio, Tilford Road, Tilford, Surrey GU10 2DZ, **506, 510, 511, 512**, Adam Gallery, 24 Cork Street, London W1S 3NJ, **865, 867**

RAE, Prof. Fiona, RA, c/o Royal Academy of Arts, **306, 308, 419, 1439**

Rae, John, 14 Orchard Street, St Albans, Hertfordshire AL3 4HL, **408**

Raeburn, Chris, Flat 16, 4 Tiltman Place, London N7 7EG, **1018**

Raitt, Neil, Flat 6, F Block, Peabody Estate, St Johns Hill, London SW11 1UJ, **56**

Rana, Rashid, Courtesy of the Artist and Lisson Gallery, London 52-54 Bell Street, London NW1 5DA, **839**

Ranson, Michelle, 14 Springfield Road, Sudbury, Suffolk CO10 1PH, **15, 283**

Ravenscroft, Ben, 101 Manwood Road, London SE4 1SA, **188, 470**

Redman, James, Flat 1, 98 Tollington Park, London N4 3RB, **1093**

Rego, Paula, c/o Marlborough Fine Art, 6 Albemarle Street, London W1S 4BY, **575, 576**

Reis, Luis Carlos, Flat 1, 2 Exeter Road, London NW2 4SP, **1139**

Rejs, Jolanta, 52 Belmont Avenue, New Malden, Surrey KT3 6QD, **530**

Relly, Tamsin, 87A Lower Marsh, London SE1 7AB, **726**

REMFRY, David, MBE RA, 19 Palace Gate, London W8 5LS, **62, 522, 1364, 1365, 1366**

Reynolds, Tom, Top Floor Flat, 44 Highgate Hill, London N19 5NQ, **1027, 1067**

Ricci, Giulia, 121B Amhurst Road, London E8 2AN, **312, 476**

Richards, Nicholas, 6 Bradgate Road, Catford, London SE6 4TS, **769**

Richards, Wesley, 35 Broadoaks Way, Bromley, Kent BR2 0UA, **1078**

Richardson, Frances, 9 Westbury Court, Nightingale Lane, London SW4 9AA, **1185, 1306**

Richardson, Leonora, Flat 2, The Copse, Fortis Green, London N2 9HL, **1301**

Richardson, Tracey, 23 Edgecombe House, Whitlock Drive, London SW19 6SL, **718**

Rideal, Liz, 2 Whittlesey Street, London SE1 8SZ, **405**

Ridgwell, Martin, 129 Upland Road, London SE22 0DF, **710**

Rigden, Geoffrey, 57 Reardon House, Reardon Street, London E1W 2QJ, **147, 1383**

RITCHIE, Prof. Ian, CBE RA, Ian Ritchie Architects, 110 Three Colt Street, London E14 8AZ, **733, 851, 852, 856**

Rizova, Aleksandrina, Flat 26, Kinetica Apartments, 12 Tyssen Street, London E8 2TE, **1039, 1042**

Robertson, Carol, c/o Flowers Gallery, 82 Kingsland Road, London E2 8DP, **379**

Robertson, Murray, 43 Gilmour Street, Eaglesham, Glasgow G76 0AA, **703**

Robinson, Hannah, 78 Stony Lane, Burton, Christchurch, Dorset BH23 7LE, **424**

Roesler, Ritva, 20 Randle Road, Richmond TW10 7LT, **1237**

ROGERS OF RIVERSIDE, Lord, CH RA, Rogers Stirk Harbour + Partners, Thames Wharf, Rainville Road, London W6 9HA, **1003, 1004, 1008, 1009, 1095, 1149**

Rolph, Danny, c/o Huguenot Editions, 8 Huguenot Place, Wandsworth, London SW18 2EN, **744**

Roman, Manuel, 8 Lohmann House, London SE11 5BU, **739**

ROONEY, Mick, RA, Fosse Gallery Fine Art, Manor House, The Square, Stow-on-the-Wold, Gloucestershire GL54 1AF, **461, 466, 931, 932, 1372, 1373**

Rose, Stephen, 26 Burnhill Road, Beckenham, Kent BR3 3LA, **256**

ROSOMAN, The late Leonard, OBE RA, Private Collection, **1376, 1379**, Lent by the National Portrait Gallery, London **1377**, Royal Academy of Arts, London **1378**, ING Commercial Banking UK, **1380**, Royal College of Art Collection, **1381**

Ross, James, 11 Empress Mews, London SE5 9BT, **367**

Rossiter, Alan, 90 Albion Drive, London E8 4LY, **1342**

Rothman, Alicia, 3 Galata Road, London SW13 9NQ, **316**

Rowan Hamilton, Sabrina, 258 Latimer Road, London W10 6QY, **997**

Rubin, Gideon, 12 Mutrix Road, London NW6 4QG, **114**

Ruffles, Marguerite, 3 Thornley Lane, Rowlands Gill, Tyne and Wear NE39 1AU, **369**

Ruyter, Lisa, Courtesy of Alan Cristea Gallery,
31 & 34 Cork Street, London W1S 3NU, **586**

Ryan, Liam, 57 Redchurch Street, London E2 7DJ, **232**

Ryan, Stephen, 13 Modder Place, London SW15 1PA, **976**

RYAN, Thomas, Hon Member Ex Officio PPRHA,
Robertstown Lodge, Robertstown, Ashbourne,
Co. Meath, Ireland, **14**

Rylands, Alison, 45 Garden Avenue, Mitcham, Surrey
CR4 2EE, **319**

S Saadeh, Raeda, c/o Rose Issa Projects, 269 Kensington
High Street, London W8 6NA, **349, 1457**

Sadeh, Juliana, 28 Parsons Mead, Norwich, Norfolk
NR4 6PG, **381**

Sadler, Margaret Ann, 7 Balliol Avenue, London E4 6LX,
711

Sah 'Azad', Govinda, c/o October Gallery,
24 Old Gloucester Street, London WC1N 3AL, **41**

Salmon, Chris, 45 Rainbow Street, London SE5 7TB, **729**

Samarasinghe, Dunisha, Flat 3, 4 Oakhill Road, London
SW15 2QU, **67**

Samuels, Allan, Mead Cottage, Milton Lilbourne, Pewsey,
Wilts SN9 5LQ, **122**

SANDLE, Prof. Michael, RA, Flat 26, De Beauvoir Place,
3 Tottenham Road, London N1 4EP, **654, 655, 656, 1242,
1243**

Sargent, Nick, The Church of St Magnus the Martyr,
Lower Thames Street, London EC3R 6DN, **161, 213**

Sarkissian, Staphan, Flat 6, Shelley House, 48 Lanhill
Road, London W9 2BY, **387**

Sato, Miho, Flat 3, 181 Bow Road, London E3 2SJ, **280, 378**

Sauerbruch Hutton Architects, Lehrter Strasse 57,
Berlin 10557, Germany, **1002**

Saull, Martin, 31 Tollgate Avenue, Redhill, Surrey
RH1 5HR, **748**

Saunders, Lynn, 90 Ravensbourne Avenue, Bromley,
Kent BR2 0AX, **609**

Savage, Percy, 23 Dyer Road, Southampton SO15 3EH, **946**

Savigny, Catherine, 163 Rue de Sèvres, Paris 75015, France, **1277**

Sawdon Smith, Richard, 1 Aldershaw, Piper Close, Off Watkinson Road, London N7 8EX, **1451**

Scarnicchia, Loriana, 287 Finchley Road, Flat 18, London NW3 6ND, **142**

Schelenz, Silke, The Orchards, 94 Denmark Street, Diss, Norfolk IP22 4LF, **619**

Schinagl, Daniel, 18 Hunyadi Janos Utca, Budapest H-1028, Hungary, **1014**

Schosser, Karin, 17 Disraeli Road, London W5 5HS, **361**

Scully, Sean, Collection of the Artist, **847, 863**

Sendell, Poppy, 87 Erpingham Road, London SW15 1BJ, **175**

Seow, James, 12C Jackson Road, London N7 6EJ, **538**

SETCH, Terry, RA, 111 Plymouth Road, Penarth, Vale of Glamorgan CF64 5DF, **90, 144, 444, 1370**

Shapira, Aithan, 5505 NE Simpson Street, Portland, Oregon 97218, USA, **680**

Shaw, George, c/o Hole Editions, 36 Lime Street, Ouseburn, Newcastle, NE1 2PQ, **453, 546**

Shaw, Phil, 54A Brondesbury Villas, Basement Flat, London NW6 6AB, **545**

Shaw, Raqib, Courtesy of the Artist and White Cube, **1323**

Shaw, Rob, Potter's Cottage, Beckside, 1 Wesley Square, Staithes, Saltburn, Cleveland TS13 5BT, **904**

Shaw, Tim, Chyglidden, Higher Spargo, Mabe, Penryn, Cornwall TR10 9JQ, **1305**

Shawcross, Neil, 4 Inns Court, Hillsborough, County Down, BT26 6AQ, Northern Ireland, **869**

Shepherd, Dominic, 108 Morden Park Cottage, Nr. Wareham, Dorset BH20 7DJ, **102**

Shichkov, Igor, 9 Podsosenksiy per, Flat 28, Moscow 105062, Russia, **613**

Shields, Mark, c/o Grosvenor Gallery, London, **1338**

Shiomi, Nana, 96A Greenvale Road, London SE9 1PF, **584, 585**

Shobowale, Olu, 67 Plevna Crescent, London N15 6DX, **439, 840**

Showghi, Batool, 100 Walton Avenue, Harrow, Middlesex HA2 8QX, **800**

Shread, Peter, 6 Clark Street, Stourbridge, Worcestershire DY8 3UF, **529**

Simms, Alexandra, Studio A, 27 St John's Lane, London ECIM 4BU, **1454**

Sims, Ron, Bugle Cottage, 123 Tilkey Road, Coggeshall, Essex CO6 1QN, **69, 134**

Sinclair, Perdita, Robertson Yard, 42A Robertson Road, Brighton BN1 5NJ, **430**

Singporewala, Karl, 30 Town Barn Road, Crawley, West Sussex RH11 7EB, **1138**

Skinner, Nicola, 44 Blackhorse Lane, Hitchin, Herts SG4 9EN, **348**

Sleigh, Bronwen, Flat 2/2, 5 Wilton Drive, Glasgow G20 6RW, **783, 786**

Small, David, 164C Stroud Green Road, London N4 3RS, **116, 266**

Smith, Angela, 6 Juggs Close, Lewes, East Sussex BN7 1QP, **222**

Smith, Craig, 23 Hill Court, Surbiton KT6 4LW, **1099**

Smith, Ivy, 77 City Road, Norwich NR1 3AS, **723**

Smith, Kiki, Courtesy of the Artist and Timothy Taylor Gallery, London, and Pace Gallery, New York, **1474**

Smith, Richard, c/o Flowers Gallery, 82 Kingsland Road, London E2 8DP, **121**

Smith, Wendy, 2 Little Brownings, London SE23 3XJ, **237, 474**

Smith Polyblank, Emily, Old Church School, The Street, Shadoxhurst, Ashford, Kent TN26 1LU, **539**

Snaebjornsson, Gardar, Giljaland 25, Reykjavik, 108, Iceland, **468**

Snell, Robin, 22 Abbey Gardens, London NW8 9AT, **1123**

Sole, Terence, 178 Mortimer Street, Herne Bay, Kent CT6 5DT, **459**

Spare, Richard, 72 Ravensbourne Park, London SE6 4XZ, **705**

Spatial Affairs Bureau, 102 Ravenhurst Road, Birmingham B17 9DP, **1025**

Spens, Peter, 3 Cranley Gardens, London N10 3AA, **886**

Squire and Partners, 77 Wicklow Street, London WC1X 9JY, **1144**

Stahl, Andrew, 1 Old Oak Road, London W3 7HN, **71, 140**

Stanford, Fianne, 85 High Street, Burnham on Crouch, Essex CM0 8AH, **502**

Stanley, William, Flat 16, 32 Kingswood Drive, London SE19 1UR, **1111**

Stanton Williams, 36 Graham Street, London N1 8GJ, **1066**

Stark, Ashley, 38 Morton Road, London N1 3BD, **621**

Stark, John, 47A Princess May Road, London N16 8DF, **449**

Stein, William, 19 Kings Road, London NW10 2BL, **172**

Stirling, Kitty, 83 Leighton Gardens, London NW10 3PY, **374**

Stjernsward, Philippa, 181B Lavender Hill, London SW11 5TE, **6**

Stokes, Anthony, 21 Prospect Place, Ogmore Vale, Bridgend CF32 7DE, **949**

Stokes, David, 11 Wolsey Close, Southall, Middlesex UB2 4NQ, **135**

Stronach, Iain, 71 Great Dell, Welwyn Garden City, Herts AL8 7HP, **482**

Stubbs, David, 133 Latimer Road, Eastbourne, East Sussex BN22 7JB, **236**

Studio 8 Architects, 95 Greencroft Gardens, London NW6 3PG, **980, 1112**

Sullivan, David, 35 Mount Echo Avenue, Chingford, London E4 7JX, **358**

Sumi, Michiko, 12B Stanbury Court, 99 Haverstock Hill, London NW3 4RP, **1022**

Summers, Ash, 43 Cannon Street, Little Downham, Ely, Cambridgeshire CB6 2SS, **956**

SuperFusionLab, 59 Banner Street, London EC1Y 8PX, **1127**

Sures, Hans Heinrich, 23 Barrington Road, London N8 8QT, **323**

Surey, Philip, 8 Kings Grove, London SE15 2NB, **1161**

Surface Architects Ltd, 51 Scrutton Street, London EC2A 4PJ, **1044**

Sutcliffe-Fuller, Catherine, 11 Elmpark Vale, Stockton Lane, York YO31 1DU, **766**

Sutherland-Beatson, Julian, The Studio, 3 Dittons Road, Eastbourne, Sussex BN21 1DN, **372**

SUTTON, Philip, RA, 3 Morfa Terrace, Manorbier, Tenby, Pembrokeshire SA70 7TH, **3, 50, 51, 962, 1409**

Sutton, Trevor, 5 The Colonnades, 105 Wilton Way, London E8 1BH, **385, 605, 961**

Swann, Richard, 100A High Street, Hastings, East Sussex TN34 3ES, **225, 342**

Sweetlove, William, Nieuwpoortsteenweg 155, Koksÿde, 8670, Belgium, **1297**

Syed, Farah, 81 Southey Road, London N15 5LJ, **252, 509**

Sykes, Sandy, 1 Dunbards Cottage, East End Road, Bradwell-on-Sea, Essex CMO 7PS, **1354**

Szczepaniak, Nicholas, 18 Wordsworth Place, Dronfield, Derbyshire S18 1NL, **977, 978**

Szerszynska, Jasia, 144 Haberdasher Street, London N1 6EJ, **678, 692**

T

Takada, Suguru, Seto-Shi, Shinto-Cho 2, Aichi-Ken Seto-Shi, 489-0058, Japan, **1194**

Takizawa, Akiko, Flat 6, Archbishop Coggan House, 2 Belmont Park, London SE13 5DS, **595**

Tang, Martin, 21 Forbes Way, Ruislip HA4 9LP, **983**

Tanna, Neal, Flat 14C, 66-68 King Williams Walk, London SE10 9JW, **972**

Tarbet, Robin, 25 Rectory Mews, off Evering Road, London N16 7QL, **57**

Taylor, Brian, 5 Tressillian Crescent, London SE4 1QJ, **1204**

Tebbenhoff, Almuth, 60 Standen Road, London SW18 5TQ, **1273**

Tennyson, Michael, 36 Sunningdale Road, Bromsgrove B61 7NN, **1147**

Teo Boon Ting, Wendy, 13 Bowsted Court, Parkham Road, London SW11 3JP, **1125**

Tesic, Biljana, 10B Leopold Road, London W5 3PB, **741**

Theobald, Stephanie, 73 Richmond Road, London E8 3AA, **11**

Thomas, Emily, 35 Watford Road, Northwood, Middlesex HA6 3NX, **719**

Thomas, Guy, 9 St Johns Road Lower Weston, Bath BA1 3BN, **1275, 1311**

Thomas, Nancy, 376 Court Road, Orpington, Kent BR6 9BX, **1346**

Thompson, Estelle, Courtesy of Purdy Hicks Gallery, London, **1443**

Thornburn, Victoria, Coffee House, Market Square, Kineton, Warwick CV35 0LP, **804**

TILSON, Joe, RA, Courtesy of Alan Cristea Gallery, 31 & 34 Cork Street, London W1S 3NU, **638, 639, 640,** Courtesy of Marlborough Fine Art Ltd, 6 Albemarle Street, London W1S 4BY, **49, 1411, 1416,**

TINDLE, Dr David, RA, c/o The Redfern Gallery, 20 Cork Street, London W1S 3HL , **40, 63, 76, 241, 1407, 1470**

Tingle, Mike, 29 Applegarth Avenue, Newton Abbot, Devon TQ12 1RP, **704**

Tinsley, Francis, 28 Ewell Court Avenue, Epsom, Surrey KT19 0DZ, **485, 958**

Tom, Mathew, 18 St Norbert Green, London SE4 2HD, **1337**

Tonkin Liu, 5 Wilmington Square, London WC1X 0ES, **1137**

Tony Fretton Architects, 109-123 Clifton Street, London EC2A 4LD, **1053, 1054**

Ward, Ellen, Rosemarie, Roman Road, Dorking, Surrey RH4 3ET, **1035**

Ward, Elly, 7 Ducie Street, London SW4 7RP, **1098**

Ware, Robert, 1D Wilberforce Mews, Stonhouse Street, London SW4 6BD, **1048**

Waskett, Tim, 5 Charlotte House, 9 Fairfax Mews, London E16 1TY, **255**

Waters, Thomas, Apple Tree Cottage, 19 Sand Lane, Northill, Bedfordshire SG18 9AD, **77**

Watt, Alison, Courtesy of the Artist and Ingleby Gallery, 15 Calton Road, Edinburgh EH8 8DL, **859, 871**

WEARING, Gillian, OBE RA, Maureen Paley, 21 Herald Street, London E2 6JT, **818**

Webb, Anne, 75 Station Road, Fordham, Ely, Cambridgeshire CB7 5LP, **229**

Webb, David, APT Studios, 6 Creekside, London SE8 4SA, **155, 397**

Webb, Mary, Watsons Farm, Cratfield Road, Fressingfield, Eye, Suffolk IP21 5SH, **346**

Webb, Richard Kenton, The Coach House, Fraziers Folly, Siddington, Cirencester, Gloucestershire GL7 6HR, **209, 210**

Weir, Jacqueline, 68c Marchmont Street, London WC1N 1AB, **214**

Welch, Robert, 2 Sunfields Place, Blackheath, London SE3 8SP, **101, 354**

Welchman, Sally, c/o I O Gallery, 39 Sydney Street, Brighton, Sussex BN1 4EP, **377**

Westgate, Gillian, 73 South Road, Dover CT17 0DN, **777**

Whicheloe, Oscar, Chalfont, Hillbrow Road, Esher, Surrey KT10 9UD, **725**

WHISHAW, Anthony, RA, 7A Albert Place, Victoria Road, London W8 5PD, **250, 902, 903, 1415**

White, Bish, 7 Fernshaw Road, London SW10 0TB, **1347**

White, Rob, c/o Huguenot Editions, 8 Huguenot Place, London SW18 2EN, **650**

White, Stephen, 6 Nab Wood Crescent, Shipley, West Yorkshire BD18 4HX, **1206**

Whitehouse, Vanessa, 40 Upper Fant Road, Maidstone, Kent ME16 8DN, **115**

Whittlesea, Michael, 98 Defoe House, Barbican, London EC2Y 8ND, **164, 292**

Wiener, Jenny, Studio 160, 8 Shepherd Market, London W1K 1AZ, **555, 556**

Wiggins, Toby, 4 Alexandra Terrace, Cowlease, Swanage, Dorset BH19 2QQ, **104, 498**

Wignall, James, 23 Rossett Way, Harrogate, North Yorkshire HG2 0EE, **1313**

WILDING, Alison, RA, c/o Karsten Schubert, 5-8 Lower John Street, Golden Square, London W1F 9DR, **1252**

WILKINSON, Chris, OBE RA, Wilkinson Eyre Architects, 33 Bowling Green Lane, London EC1R 0BJ, **1, 934, 1134, 1141, 1142**

Williams, Brigitte, Rushdene House, Dene Road, Ashtead, Surrey KT21 1EE, **47, 150**

Williams, Emyr, 11 Old Church Road, East Hanningfield, Chelmsford, Essex CM3 8BE, **78**

Wilson, Kate, 7 Hotham Road, London SW19 1BS, **428, 429**

Wilson, Keith, The Gardens, Ballycastle, Mayo, Ireland, **436, 857**

Wilson, Keith, 60B Trinity Church Square, London SE1 4HT, **1216, 1230**

Wilson, Nevill, 7 Duddingston Park, Edinburgh EH15 1JN, **176**

WILSON, Prof. Richard, RA, 44 Banyard Road, London SE16 2YA, **582, 1136, 1362**

Winder-Boyle, Ann, 9 Crabtree Close, Beaconsfield, Bucks HP9 1UQ, **267**

Winkelman, Joseph, 69 Old High Street, Oxford OX3 9HT, **717**

Winstanley, Paul, Courtesy of Alan Cristea Gallery, 31 & 34 Cork Street, London W1S 3NU, **590**

Winston, Willow, Unit 17, Excelsior Works, Rollins Street, London SE15 1EP, **281, 282**

Winthrop, David, 8 Station Approach Road, Ramsgate, Kent CT11 7RW, **314**

Woffenden, Emma, 1A Hilly Fields Crescent, London SE4 1QA, **1284, 1285**

Won, Jiho, 3 Stibbington House, Cranleigh Street, London NW1 1NS, **1160**

Wood, Christopher, 1 Norfolk Place, Chapel Allerton, Leeds, West Yorkshire, LS7 4PT, **335**

Woodall, David, The Studio, Upper Court Road, Woldingham, Caterham, Surrey CR3 7BF, **177, 231**

Woodcock, Rosie, Alpha House, Tredinnick, Duloe, Liskeard, Cornwall PL14 4PJ, **275**

Woodcock-Jones, Tim, 18 Albany Road, Bedford, Bedfordshire, MK40 3PH, **145**

WOODROW, Bill, RA, c/o Royal Academy of Arts, **1298, 1299**

Woods, Jean, 24 Churchfields, West Mersea, Mersea Island, Nr. Colchester, Essex CO5 8QJ, **797**

Woods, Richard, Courtesy of Alan Cristea Gallery, 31 & 34 Cork Street, London W1S 3NU, **588**

Woolston, Derek, 12 Aetheric Road, Braintree, Essex CM7 2NF, **271**

WRAGG, John, RA, 6 Castle Lane, Devizes, Wiltshire, SN10 1HJ, **28, 29, 30, 244, 248, 359**

Wright, Eleanor, 5 Ackroyd Drive, London E3 4JY, **1236**

Wright, Everton, 68 Clive Road, London SE21 8BY, **908**

Wright, Lisa, Chapel House, Crelly, Helston, Cornwall TR13 0EY, **935**

Wright, Simon, 41 Melton Road, Wymondham, Norfolk NR18 0DB, **149, 404**

Wright, William, 13B Kilmorie Road, London SE23 2SS, **497**

Y   Yahya, Mohd Norhakim, 98 Ashbourne Road, Mitcham, Surrey CR4 2BB, **258**

Yamada, Haruko, Flat 3.4 Pulse Apartments, 52 Lymington Road, London NW6 1HQ, **1231**

Supporting the Royal Academy

Supporting the Royal Academy

The Royal Academy of Arts receives no annual government funding
and is entirely reliant on self-generated income and charitable support.
Registered Charity No. 1125383

The Royal Academy Trust

Registered Charity No. 1067270

The Royal Academy Trust was founded in 1981 to receive, invest and disburse
funds given in support of the Royal Academy of Arts. Since then the Trust has
raised an endowment fund that now amounts to nearly £26 million, the income
from which helps to finance the Academy's charitable activities, and has
obtained funding totalling almost £60 million for capital projects, including
the creation of the Sackler Wing of Galleries. The recent phase of works
included the restoration of and improvements to the Main Galleries,
the Annenberg Courtyard and the John Madejski Fine Rooms, open to
the public for exhibitions from the newly catalogued and conserved Royal
Academy Permanent Collection.

Become a Patron

The Royal Academy's Patrons Groups form a vital source of income in the
absence of public funding. The Patrons Groups maintain and develop the
Academy's internationally renowned exhibition programme; fund education
projects for children, families and people with special needs; provide
scholarships and bursaries for art students in the Royal Academy Schools;
and help to conserve the Academy's unique Permanent Collection.

Further information on charitable giving to the Royal Academy
can be obtained from Charlotte Appleyard, Head of Patrons, on
020 7300 5977, or from Kathleen Hearst, American Associates of the
Royal Academy Trust, 555 Madison Avenue, Suite 1300, New York,
NY 10022, USA.

Leaving a gift to the Royal Academy in your will

If you would like to protect the Royal Academy so that future generations can
enjoy its treasures, please consider leaving a gift to the Academy in your will.

A gift can be a sum of money, a specific item or a share of what is left
after you have provided for your family and friends. Any gift, large or small,
is greatly appreciated and will help us to continue our tradition of artistic
excellence into the future.

For more information please contact Emma Warren-Thomas on
020 7300 5677, or at legacies@royalacademy.org.uk

Corporate opportunities

Since its foundation in 1768 the Academy has remained both independent and self-supporting, receiving no government funding for its exhibitions or education programmes.

The Academy has successfully led the fields of arts sponsorship, corporate membership and corporate entertaining for around 30 years. Together, these aspects make a significant financial contribution, enabling the Academy to maintain both the excellent artistic reputation for which it is known and its home, Burlington House, and to fulfil the role that it plays in the cultural life of this country.

Since 1979 the Academy has worked with over 200 sponsors in a range of areas, including exhibitions, education, fundraising events and the Royal Academy Schools. The Project Giving team also looks after 60 Corporate Members who enjoy numerous benefits for their staff, clients and community partners.

Sponsorship and corporate membership can offer companies:
- Priority booking of and exclusive entertaining in the Royal Academy's suite of eighteenth-century Fine Rooms, for business presentations, breakfasts or dinners combined with private views of exhibitions.
- Comprehensive crediting on all publicity material and involvement with press and promotions campaigns (sponsorship only).
- Invitations to prestigious Royal Academy corporate and social events.
- Special passes for unlimited entry to all Royal Academy exhibitions.
- Free entry for employees; behind-the-scenes tours; lectures and workshops for staff and their families.
- Regular monitoring and evaluation.
- A dedicated team of experienced staff to manage every aspect of sponsorship, corporate membership and corporate entertaining.

Further details are available from the Project Giving Office on 020 7300 5629/5979.

Royal Academy Trust

Registered Charity No. 1067270

American Associates of the Royal Academy Trust

Japanese Committee of Honour

Corporate Members

Mr Nobuyuki Idei (J Concept) and Mrs Idei
Mr Yoshitoshi Kitajima (Dai Nippon Printing Co Ltd) and Mrs Kitajima
Mr Shinzo Maeda and Mrs Maeda
Mr Yoshihiko Miyauchi (ORIX Corporation) and Mrs Miyauchi
Mr Yuzaburo Mogi (Kikkoman Corporation) and Mrs Mogi
Mrs Yoshiko Mori (Mori Building Co Ltd)
Mr Takeo Obayashi (Obayashi Corporation) and Mrs Obayashi
Mr Nobutada Saji (Suntory Limited) and Mrs Saji
Mrs Takako Suzuki
Mr Toichi Takenaka (Takenaka Corporation) and Mrs Takenaka
Mr Yuzo Yagi (Yagi Tsusho Ltd) and Mrs Yagi

Patrons

Mr Hiroaki Fujii (*Chair*) and Mrs Fujii
Prof Tadao Ando HON RA and Mrs Ando
Mr Akito Arima and Mrs Arima
Mr Shinji Fukukawa and Mrs Fukukawa
Prof Arata Isozaki HON RA and Mrs Isozaki
Mr Hideo Morita and Mrs Morita
Mr Koichi Nezu and Mrs Nezu
Mr Yoji Shimizu and Mrs Shimizu
Mr Masayoshi Son and Mrs Son
Mr Jonathan Stone and Mrs Stone
Mr Hideya Taida HON CBE and Mrs Taida
Mr Shuji Takashina and Mrs Takashina
Mr Tsuneharu Takeda and Mrs Takeda
Mr Hiroyasu Tomita and Mrs Tomita
Mrs Yasuko Yamazaki
Mrs Yu Serizawa (*Director*)

Royal Academy Supporters

The Trustees of the Royal Academy Trust are grateful to all its donors for their continued loyalty and generosity. They would like to extend their thanks to all those who have made a significant commitment, past and present, to the galleries, the exhibitions, the conservation of the Permanent Collection, the Library collections, the Royal Academy Schools, the Learning programme and other specific appeals.

Major Benefactors

HM The Queen
Her Majesty's Government
The 29th May 1961 Charitable Trust
The Aldama Foundation
The American Associates of the Royal Academy Trust
The Annenberg Foundation
Barclays Bank
BAT Industries plc
Sir David and Lady Bell
The late Tom Bendhem
The late Brenda M Benwell-Lejeune
John Frye Bourne
British Telecom
The Brown Foundation
John and Susan Burns
Mr Raymond M Burton CBE
Sir Trevor Chinn CVO and Lady Chinn
The Trustees of the Clore Foundation
The John S Cohen Foundation
Sir Harry and Lady Djanogly
The Dulverton Trust
Alfred Dunhill Limited
The John Ellerman Foundation
The Eranda Foundation
Ernst & Young
Esso UK plc
Esmée Fairbairn Charitable Trust
The Fidelity UK Foundation
The Foundation for Sports and the Arts

Friends of the Royal Academy
Jacqueline and Michael Gee
The Getty Grant Programme
Mr Thomas Gibson
Glaxo Holdings plc
Diane and Guilford Glazer
Mr and Mrs Jack Goldhill
Maurice and Laurence Goldman
The Horace W Goldsmith Foundation
HRH Princess Marie-Chantal of Greece
Mr and Mrs Jocelin Harris
The Philip and Pauline Harris Charitable Trust
The Charles Hayward Foundation
Heritage Lottery Fund
IBM United Kingdom Limited
The Idlewild Trust
Lord and Lady Jacobs
The JP Jacobs Charitable Trust
The Japan Foundation
Gabrielle Jungels-Winkler Foundation
Mr and Mrs Donald Kahn
The Lillian Jean Kaplan Foundation
The Kresge Foundation
The Samuel H Kress Foundation
The Kirby Laing Foundation
The Lankelly Foundation
The late Mr John S Latsis

Patrons of the Royal Academy Trust

In recent years the Royal Academy has established several Patrons Groups to encourage the regular and committed support of individuals who believe in the Royal Academy's mission to promote the widest possible understanding and enjoyment of the visual arts.

The Royal Academy is delighted to thank all its Patrons for generously supporting exhibitions, Learning, the Royal Academy Schools, the Permanent Collection and Library, and Anglo-American initiatives over the past year, and for assisting in the general upkeep of the Academy, with donations of £1,500 and more.

Royal Academy Patrons

Chair	Lord Davies of Abersoch CBE	
Platinum Patrons	Genevieve and Peter Davies Mr and Mrs Patrick Doherty Ms Ghizlan El Glaoui	Mrs Nina Hirji Kheraj Mr and Mrs Jake Shafran David and Sophie Shalit

Gold Patrons	Mr Edward Atkin CBE and
	    Mrs Celia Atkin
	Mr and Mrs William Brake
	Ms Linda Cooper
	Lord and Lady Davies of Abersoch
	Mr and Mrs Andrew Higginson
	Mrs Elizabeth Hosking
	Sir Sydney Lipworth QC and
	    Lady Lipworth CBE
		Mr and Mrs Ronald Lubner
		Mr Scott Mead
		Sir Keith and Lady Mills
		Lady Rayne
		Lady Renwick
		Mrs Stella Shawzin
		Mrs Elyane Stilling

Silver Patrons	Lady Agnew Mrs Nancy Al Zain Miss H J C Anstruther Lord Ashburton Edgar Astaire Mr and Mrs Simon Bamber Jane Barker Stephen Barry Charitable Settlement Ms Catherine Baxendale The Duke of Beaufort	Mrs Gary Brass Mr and Mrs Richard Briggs OBE Mrs Elie Brihi Mrs Marcia Brocklebank Lady Brown Mr and Mrs Charles H Brown Jeremy Brown Lord Browne of Madingley Mr Martin Burton Mr F A A Carnwath CBE

Jean and Eric Cass
Sir Charles and Lady Chadwyck-
Healey
Mr David Cheyne
Sir Trevor Chinn cvo and Lady
Chinn
Mr and Mrs George Coelho
Denise Cohen Charitable Trust
Sir Ronald Cohen
Mrs Jennifer Cooke
Mark and Cathy Corbett
Julian Darley and Helga Sands
The Countess of Dartmouth
Mr Daniel Davies
Dr Anne Dornhorst
Lord Douro
Ms Noreen Doyle
Janet and Maurice Dwek
Mrs Sheila Earles
Dr Yvonne von Egidy-Winkler and
Mr Peter Philip Winkler
Lord and Lady Egremont
Benita and Gerald Fogel
Mrs Rosamund Fokschaner
Mrs Marion F Foster
Mrs Anthony Foyle
Mr and Mrs Eric Franck
Arnold Fulton
Mr and Mrs Spencer Fung
The Lord Gavron cbe
Jacqueline and Jonathan Gestetner
Lady Getty
Mr Mark Glatman
Lady Gosling
Mr Stephen Gosztony
Piers Gough cbe ra
Mr Gavin Graham
HRH Princess Marie-Chantal of
Greece
Peter and Andrea De Haan
Mr James Hambro
Sir Ewan and Lady Harper
Mrs Melanie Harris
Sir John Hegarty and Miss Philippa
Crane
Michael and Morven Heller

Mr Mark Hendriksen
Lady Heseltine
Mr and Mrs Alan Hobart
Mr Patrick Holmes
Mr Philip Hudson
Mr and Mrs Jon Hunt
Mrs Pauline Hyde
Mrs Deanna Ibrahim
S Isern-Feliu
Mrs Caroline Jackson
Mr Michael Jacobson
Sir Martin and Lady Jacomb
Mrs Raymonde Jay
Mr and Mrs Sidney Jefcoate
Fiona Johnstone
Mr Nicholas Jones
Mrs Ghislaine Kane
Miss Joanna Kaye
Dr Elisabeth Kehoe
Mr Duncan Kenworthy obe
Princess Jeet Khemka
Mr Gerald Kidd
Mr D H Killick
Mr and Mrs James Kirkman
Mrs Aboudi Kosta
Mr and Mrs Herbert Kretzmer
Norman A Kurland and Deborah
A David
The de Laszlo Foundation
Joan H Lavender
Mrs Rachel Laxer
Mr George Lengvari and Mrs Inez
Lengvari
Lady Lever of Manchester
Mr Peter Lloyd
Miss R Lomax-Simpson
The Marquess of Lothian
The Hon Mrs Virginia Lovell
Mr and Mrs Henry Lumley
Mrs Josephine Lumley
Mrs Sally Lykiardopulo
Mrs I C McAlpine
Gillian McIntosh
Andrew and Judith McKinna
Mr Nicholas Maclean
Sally and Donald Main

Mrs Sally Major
Mrs Inge Margulies
Mr and Mrs Richard Martin
Zvi and Ofra Meitar Family Fund
Professor Anthony Mellows OBE TD
   and Mrs Anthony Mellows
Mrs Ann Miller
Mrs Joy Moss
Mr Michael Moszynski
Mrs Carole Myers
Marion and Guy Naggar
Dr Ann Naylor
Ann Norman-Butler
Mr Michael Palin
John H Pattisson
Nicholas B Paumgarten
Mr and Mrs D J Peacock
Mr and Mrs A Perloff
Mr Philip Perry
David Pike
Mr and Mrs Anthony Pitt-Rivers
Mr and Mrs Stuart Popham
Mr Basil Postan
John and Anne Raisman
Lord Rothschild
Mr and Mrs K M Rubie
Roland Rudd
The Lady Henrietta St George
Mr Adrian Sassoon

H M Sassoon Charitable Trust
Mr and Mrs Christopher
   Satterthwaite
Carol Sellars
Mr and Mrs Kevin Senior
Dr Lewis Sevitt
Christina Countess of Shaftesbury
Mr Robert N Shapiro
Victoria Sharp
Major General and Mrs Jonathan
   Shaw
The Schneer Foundation
Richard and Veronica Simmons
Mr and Mrs Alan K Simpson
Brian D Smith
Jane Spack
Summers Art Gallery / Mrs J K M
   Bentley
Sir Hugh Sykes DL
The Tavolozza Foundation
Mr Anthony J Todd
Mr and Mrs David Turner
Miss M L Ulfane
John and Carol Wates
Mrs Angela Webb
Edna and Willard Weiss
Anthony and Rachel Williams
Mr William Winters
Ms Clare Woodman

Patron Donors	J Birr Bryan Ferry Mrs Mary Graves Mr Louis Greig Mrs Bianca Roden	The Michael H Sacher Charitable Trust *And others who wish to remain* *anonymous*

Benjamin West Patrons

Chair	Lady Judge CBE	
Platinum Patrons	Charles and Kaaren Hale	Mr Christian Levett
Gold Patrons	Marco and Francesca Assetto Lady Judge CBE	Ms Alessandra Morra Mr and Mrs John R Olsen

235

Mrs Catherine Rees
Mrs Karen Santi
Edwina Sassoon
Richard and Susan Shoylekov
Jeffery C Sugarman and Alan D H Newham

Mr Robert Suss
Ms Inna Vainshtock
Cathy Wills
Manuela and Iwan Wirth
Mr and Mrs Maurice Wolridge
Ms Cynthia Wu

Patron Donors

Lord and Lady Aldington

And others who wish to remain anonymous

Library and Collections Circle

Patron Donors

Mr Loyd Grossman
Lowell Libson

Pam and Scott Schafler

Young Patrons

Mr and Mrs Tom Davies
Kalita al Swaidi

LinLi Teh
Anna Watkins

Trusts and Foundations

Artists Collecting Society
The Atlas Fund
The Albert Van den Bergh Charitable Trust
The Bomonty Charitable Trust
The Charlotte Bonham-Carter Charitable Trust
William Brake Charitable Trust
R M Burton 1998 Charitable Trust
C H K Charities Limited
P H G Cadbury Charitable Trust
The Carew Pole Charitable Trust
The Clore Duffield Foundation
John S Cohen Foundation
The Evan Cornish Foundation
The Sidney and Elizabeth Corob Charitable Trust
The Dovehouse Trust
The Gilbert and Eileen Edgar Foundation
The John Ellerman Foundation
The Eranda Foundation
Lucy Mary Ewing Charitable Trust
The Margery Fish Charity
The Flow Foundation

The Garfield Weston Foundation
Gatsby Charitable Foundation
The Golden Bottle Trust
The Gordon Foundation
Sue Hammerson Charitable Trust
The Charles Hayward Foundation
Heritage Lottery Fund
Hiscox
Holbeck Charitable Trust
The Harold Hyam Wingate Foundation
The Ironmongers' Company
The Emmanuel Kaye Foundation
The Kindersley Foundation
The de Laszlo Foundation
The David Lean Foundation
The Leche Trust
The Leverhulme Trust
The Maccabaeans
The McCorquodale Charitable Trust
The Paul Mellon Centre
The Paul Mellon Estate
The Mercers' Company
Margaret and Richard Merrell Foundation

American Associates of the Royal Academy Trust

Burlington House Trust	Mrs James C Slaughter	
Benjamin West Society	Mrs Deborah Loeb Brice Mrs Nancy B Negley	
Benefactors	Mr Michael Moritz and Ms Harriet Heyman	Mrs Edmond J Safra The Hon John C Whitehead
Sponsors	Mrs Drue Heinz HON DBE David Hockney OM CH RA Mr Arthur L Loeb Mr and Mrs Hamish Maxwell Mr and Mrs Richard J Miller Jr Diane A Nixon	Ms Joan Stern Dr and Mrs Robert D Wickham
Patrons	Mr and Mrs Steven Ausnit Mr and Mrs E William Aylward Mr Donald A Best Mrs Mildred C Brinn Mrs Benjamin Coates Lois M Collier Mr and Mrs Stanley De Forest Scott Mr and Mrs Lawrence S Friedland Mr and Mrs Leslie Garfield Ms Helen Harting Abell Dr Bruce C Horten Mr William W Karatz	The Hon Eugene A Ludwig and Dr Carol Ludwig Miss Lucy F McGrath Mr and Mrs Wilson Nolen Mrs Mary Sharp Cronson Ms Louisa Stude Sarofim Martin J Sullivan OBE Ms Britt Tidelius Mr Robert W Wilson

Friends of the Royal Academy

Patron: HRH The Duke of Edinburgh KG KT
Chairman: Ron Zeghibe

Join the Friends of the Royal Academy and enjoy free entry to
all RA exhibitions, plus...

- Invites to Preview Days before exhibitions open
  to the public
- Bring one adult family guest and up to four
  family children under 16 to any exhibition for free
- Use of the Friends Rooms
- Access to a programme of Friends events
- Receive the quarterly *RA Magazine*
- Keep up to date with the Friends e-news,
  packed with events, news and offers

To become a Friend

Visit	The Friends desk in the Front Hall
Go to	www.royalacademy.org.uk/friends
Call	020 7300 5664
E-mail	friend.enquiries@royalacademy.org.uk
Or write to	Friends Office
	Royal Academy of Arts
	FREEPOST 33WD 1057
	Piccadilly
	London W1E 6YZ

Registered Charity No. 272926

Royal Academy Corporate Membership Scheme

Registered Company No. 2216104

Launched in 1988, the Royal Academy's Corporate Membership Scheme has proved highly successful. Corporate Membership offers company benefits to staff, clients and community partners and access to the Academy's facilities and resources. The outstanding support we receive from companies via the scheme is vital to the continuing success of the Academy and we thank all our Members for their valuable support and continued enthusiasm.

Premier Level Members

A T Kearney Limited
Barclays plc
British Airways
CBRE
Christie's
Deutsche Bank AG
FTI Consulting
GlaxoSmithKline plc
Insight Investment
JM Finn & Co
Jones Lang LaSalle
JTI
KPMG
Lombard Odier Darier Hentsch
Neptune Investment Management
Schroders Private Banking
Smith and Williamson

Corporate Members

All Nippon Airways
BGC Partners
Bloomberg LP
BNP Paribas
Bonhams 1793 Ltd
The Boston Consulting Group UK LLP
British American Tobacco
BUPA
Capital International Limited
Clifford Chance LLP
Coca Cola Retail Research Council
Crédit Agricole CIB
Ernst & Young
F & C Asset Management plc
GAM
Generation Investment Management LLP
GKN Aerospace
Heidrick & Struggles
Hermès GB
Jefferies International
John Lewis Partnership
J P Morgan
La Mania
Lazard
Lend Lease Limited
Lindsell Train
Lloyds TSB Private Banking
Lubbock Fine Chartered Accountants
Marie Curie
Moelis & Co
Morgan Stanley
Northern Trust
Pentland Group plc
Realty Insurances Limited
Rio Tinto

243

Sponsors of Past Exhibitions

The President and Council of the Royal Academy would like to thank the following sponsors and benefactors for their generous support of major exhibitions during the last ten years:

A T Kearney
ABNAMRO
Akkök Group of Companies
American Associates of the Royal
    Academy Trust
American Express
Aygaz
Bank of America
The Bank of New York Mellon
Bastyan
BBC Radio 3
Blain Southern
Blavatnik Family Foundation
Blueprint
BNP Paribas
British American Tobacco
Canon
Carlsberg UK Ltd
Castello di Reschio
Christie's
Classic FM
Corus
J F Costopoulos Foundation
Country Life
Cox & Kings
The Daily Telegraph
Daniel Katz Gallery
Danske Bank
Guy Dawson
Deutsche Bank AG
E.ON
Ernst & Young
Eurohypo AG
Farrow & Ball

Fidelity Foundation
Lucy Flemming McGrath
Foster + Partners
Garanti Bank
Glasgow Museums
GlaxoSmithKline
Goldman Sachs International
The Great Britain Sasakawa
    Foundation
Guardian
Hauser & Wirth
The Hellenic Foundation
Hungarofest
The Independent
Insight Investment
The Japan Foundation
Lassa Tyres
A G Leventis Foundation
Harvey and Allison McGrath
Mexico Tourism Board
Mizuho International plc
Stavros Niarchos Foundation
Novo Nordisk
OAK Foundation Denmark
OTP Bank
Pemex
RA Exhibition Patrons Group
Region Holdings
Simon and Virginia Robertson
Sotheby's
The Spectator
Spoonfed
Time Out
Toshiba International Foundation

UBS Wealth Management   Walker Morris
Villa Budapest   Welcome to Yorkshire

Other sponsors Carlisle Group plc   Michael Hopkins & Partners
(sponsors   Country Life   IBJ International plc
of events,   Derwent Valley Holdings plc   Martin Krajewski
publications   John Doyle Construction   Marks & Spencer
and other items Dresdner Kleinwort Wasserstein Morgan Stanley Dean Witter
in the past   Goldman Sachs International   Newton Investment Management
five years)   Gome International   Prada
                   Gucci Group   Radisson Edwardian Hotels
                   Rob van Helden   Richard and Ruth Rogers
                   Hines   The Wine Studio

Royal Academy Schools

The Royal Academy Schools provide the only three-year postgraduate course in Fine Art in the United Kingdom. The criteria for acceptance are positive commitment and a convincing potential for creative development. This is a small, exceptional school with a challenging atmosphere of experimentation and strong sense of identity.

The Schools attract a comprehensive range of visiting tutors, both practitioners and theorists, and there exists within the studios an ongoing atmosphere of critical debate and forward-looking inquiry.

The traditional forms of painting, sculpture and printmaking are pursued alongside such newer media as digital printing in a state-of-the-art Epson suite and with facilities for photography and video.

There are no fees and students are assisted financially in a limited way by means of a variety of awards, prizes and travel bursaries.

The Schools' central-London location and close proximity to the remarkable international-standard exhibition programme of the Royal Academy in Burlington House greatly enhance the rich cultural and educational environment that exists here.

Library

The Library of the Royal Academy is for the use of its Members, staff and students, and is open for specialist research by appointment.

Telephone: 020 7300 5737
E-mail: library@royalacademy.org.uk

AGBI

Artists' General Benevolent Institution
Burlington House
Piccadilly
London W1J 0BB

Patron: HRH The Prince of Wales

Founded in 1814 by J M W Turner, the AGBI provides help to professional artists and their dependants in time of trouble.

Funds are always needed and donations of any amount are gratefully received and acknowledged. Cheques should be sent to the Secretary at the above address.

Registered Charity No. 212667
Contact: 020 7734 1193
www.agbi.org.uk

Notes

Compiled by Natalie Bouloudis, Edith Devaney,
    Lorna Dryden, Kathryn McNerny, Josephine New,
    Katherine Oliver, Jessica Parry, Rebecca Pollack,
    Paul Sirr and Jessica Smith
Production by Abbie Coppard and Sally Goble
Designed by Adam Brown_01.02
Printed by Tradewinds

Published by RA Publications
Royal Academy of Arts
Piccadilly
London W1J 0BD